AutoTalk for Women

Shirley Kachur

Foreword by Martha Billes

Published by Horse & Musket Ltd.
E-mail: horse.musket@attcanada.net

Canadian Cataloguing-in-Publication Data:

Kachur, Shirley, 1955 –
    AutoTalk for Women

ISBN 0-9685241-0-9

1. Automobiles – Maintenance and Repair   2. Automobile driving

I.   Title

TL152.K32 1999   629.28'72   C99-910432-2

Carleen Illustration   Philip Dente
                            ppd@sunlink.net

Cover Design   Silverpoint Graphics Group Inc.

Design Production   Mo Keshavjee

Editor   Lori Burwash

Printed and bound in Canada

Dedicated to my daughter, Kyla
A "next-generation" driver

For Rick, my husband, who gently insisted I proceed with
AutoTalk for Women

To Kye, my dog; I appreciated his licks and wags

In memory of Mom
Who stood beside Dad many a time with wrenches in hand

Foreword
by Martha Billes

As the Controlling Shareholder of Canadian Tire, "Canadian males" favorite store, I am often asked what it is like to be in such a position. Actually the present is simply a piece of an ongoing continuum, my life with The Tire. Tires and all the bits and pieces that serve our automobile oriented society have been a dominant part of my life. Let me share a memory or two with you.

During my childhood the family car was a source of thrills and fascination for me. I remember the first family outing in Mom's beautiful new Dodge sedan, I was three years of age. The car's sleek body was blue like shimmering water and the interior perfumed by new paint and oiled leather. I can still remember the sumptuous joy of our first ride!

And oh how I craved for a ride in the 'Rumble seat' of dad's shiny black Buick coupe, but alas that was a thrill reserved only for the boys and denied this four year old daughter. Inside wasn't so bad, perched there on mom's knee feeling quite the little princess.

In junior high school, my home room grade nine teacher thought it a good 'life skills' exercise to take the class for a show and tell of the mysteries that lie beneath the hood of the automobile. And so the whole class dutifully marched onto the playing field to where our beloved teacher had brought his car. (This was before the days of such modern inventions as windshield washers, alternators and fuel injection, car engines were, by today's standard, fairly simple.) I could feel my fellow students watching me. They must have been thinking that cars were something that I would know about. I was the daughter of the Canadian Tire family.

As for me I was confident when the hood was elevated and the spring sunshine illuminated the engine compartment of the Chev revealing its engine, a V-6. I had seen all this before. My older brother a car hobbyist had explained it all to me one hot summer day several years before.

Ah yes, that was my big brother's summer project. He, having talked on and on all through the winter months about his summer project, my brother Fred had set about to rebuild the engine of his 1946 Chevy sedan. The car was then a road worn veteran of seven or eight years of business and family travel. I remember that sultry afternoon when mom had some errands to run. I successfully begged out of tagging along. So there was brother Fred, a responsible sixteen or seventeen year old grease monkey saddled with me watching over his shoulder as he toiled. His pesky pre-teen sister whose nose was always getting into everything, now was thrust into the midst of his hobby.

I had promised mom that I'd stay out of the way. So I stood as still and as silently as I could, in awe of both his strength and his audacity. Carefully, piece by piece he dismembered the workings of the venerable old car's engine, washed and laid each one out on the floor of the garage. Row after row. "What if he can't get it back together?" I thought. But I dared not utter any such blasphemy in big brother's presence. Oh, I was afraid for him! Yet I was absolutely wrapped up in the procedure. I can still remember my heart pounding with excitement.

I became mesmerized by the process in which such a miraculous contraption (the internal combustion engine) was being reduced to a cadre of big, small and tiny parts lined up meticulously in those rows by Fred. I mused about one day being able to do the same thing myself. Little by little my inquisitiveness took over and the questions began to tumble out. "What is this? Why is this little spring here? What does this do?"

After what must have seemed an eternity to Fred and probably distraught almost beyond civility, my oldest sibling slowly and carefully explained to me how the carbonator functioned. His words were, "For the last time Martha, it takes the gasoline, mixes it with air and makes carbon. Thus," he exclaimed, "The car goes and the part is called the CARBONATOR! And that is the last question I'm going to answer!" And so, being thus banished from the garage, off I went believing with a fair certainty that I was now somewhat knowledgeable about car engines and specifically as to the function of the carbonator.

Several springs later I was with my classmates grouped around the open hood learning about basic engine function. Such a rude awakening was in store for me. And oh I remember well the intensity of the red flush which overcame me as I heard my kindly grade nine teacher query, "Carbonator? What is that Martha?" And so naively I had fallen prey to Fred's brotherly little carburetor joke in front of all my peers.

The car is both our society's slave and its master. For some folks among us a fancy automobile is a symbol of success. For others it is a tool without which we can not live our daily lives. For me the smell of tires (and cars) is in my blood.

We ladies can respond to the nagging little car problems in one of two ways. By 'hiding out' or by being a 'can doer'. Having made the choice to open the cover of this book, you have identified yourself as a 'can doer'. Congratulations!

You are holding a little gem in your palm! Open the pages and learn about all the things Shirley says you *really can do*.

Thanks to Shirley all of us can now be equipped to deal with the minor pains of car ownership. Please ladies, read on.

Introduction

Automobiles. Most of us cannot do without them. As women, we rely on our vehicles on a daily basis – they take us to and from work, make that weekly grocery trip a time-saving convenience, and ensure the kids get to their after-school activities on time. Ultimately, the automobile has become a practical extension of our lifestyle.

But wait. As with anything else in life, there are certain responsibilities that accompany owning a vehicle. You must be sure it is in safe running condition and you need to take precautions while behind the wheel. How do you accomplish this? By first getting to know your vehicle, inside and out.

Welcome to *AutoTalk for Women*. This user-friendly guide is here to help you. Like the physical characteristics of your vehicle, the first four sections are easy to identify - *Interior of Your Vehicle, Exterior of Your Vehicle, Under the Hood,* and *Underneath Your Vehicle.* Each section acquaints you with the workings of your automobile, while also offering practical tips to ensure it is clean and in safe working condition.

More than 50 pages of *Troubleshooting* advice follow, for when your vehicle makes unusual noises or experiences other malfunctions. Not to panic, though. For now, you can leave the major repairs to a professional mechanic. What you want to do at this point is diagnose what is happening to your vehicle so that intelligent decisions and effective action can be taken.

Behind the Wheel addresses safety issues and driving habits. A special supplement titled *The Mature Driver* reinforces the importance of re-assessing driving abilities. To assist you when travelling on Canadian roads or along the highways and byways in the United States, *Conversions* offers quick metric to imperial and imperial to metric calculation methods. To complete the book, *AutoTalk Assistant* provides valuable checklists, forms, placards, and reports to help make your experiences on the road less stressful.

AutoTalk for Women cannot be of service to you if it is left inside a dresser drawer or on a bookshelf. It can only be of value if you take what's inside these pages and make them work for you.

For information at your fingertips, place this trustworthy companion guide in the glove compartment of your vehicle. You can then be reassured it is always there for you.

Safe, courteous, and worry-free driving!

About the Author

Shirley Kachur has been involved in many aspects of the automotive industry. Her mechanical background started when she was a pre-teenager, helping Dad and brothers repair cars. Since then she has taught automotive courses for women, all the while keeping her hands under the hoods of many vehicles.

Shirley has written numerous newspaper columns discussing mechanical issues and behind the wheel responsibilities. This focus became the driving force behind *AutoTalk for Women*. Her mission statement, "To provide a service to the female driving public," blends well with her aspiration – that all women drive with a renewed sense of confidence.

Shirley welcomes your comments and suggestions. She can be e-mailed at musket@attcanada.net.

Table of Contents

Section 1
Interior of Your Vehicle

This section looks at the components inside your automobile. The air bag and seat belts are necessary for safety and child-restraint seats are part of this security. What the steering wheel holds offers many conveniences, such as the signal arm and cruise control settings. Other features inside your vehicle include the brake and gas pedals, rear-view mirror, head restraints, and transmission gears.

For specific information on the interior features of your car or multi-purpose vehicle (minivan, light truck, or sport-utility vehicle), consult the owner's manual.

SECTION ONE CONTENTS

...cont'd

Introduction

Keeping the interior of your vehicle clean is necessary for overall maintenance, but safety is a key consideration as well. Seat belt buckles can, for instance, become clogged with food particles, which affect how well the buckles snap in place. Or, toys and other loose objects may harm you and other passengers, especially children, in the event of a sudden turn or stop. What about the windows? A thin film of dirt or smoke coats them over time, so they need to be washed for you to have a clear view of what's on the road.

Turn the pages to discover more about what's inside your vehicle, as well as some maintenance and safety tips.

Dashboard

Air Bag

- Automobile manufacturers now install an air bag inside the dashboard on the passenger side, along with the air bag for the driver. Both air bags are now referred to as "next-generation," "Generation II," or "dual frontal" air bags.

- Air bags are most effective in high-speed frontal collisions.

- Air bags act as a supplemental safety device only and should never replace the use of correctly positioned seat belts.

- Passenger air bags are most effective when the passenger is seated in an upright position and as far back as possible from the dashboard (25 to 30 cm [10 to 12 in.] is the recommended minimum distance).

- Disabling the passenger side air bag is prohibited except under special circumstances, such as medical reasons. A form must be completed and forwarded to a government agency for approval.

- On-off switches for passenger side air bags are installed on vehicles that have no rear seating or a rear seat that is too small for a child-restraint seat.

Air Conditioner Settings

- The air conditioner should operate periodically when the humidity is low. When the humidity is high, the air conditioner is constantly on.

- Before turning on the air conditioner, open some windows to let hot air inside your vehicle escape.

- With the air conditioning on, there may be a slight decrease in engine speed. This is normal.

- It may look as if fog is seeping in through the interior vents when the air conditioner is on. This is moist air and not a malfunction of the air conditioner.

- If the windows fog, turn on the air conditioner for a couple of minutes to reduce the humidity inside your vehicle.

- After the air conditioner has been used, pools of liquid often form underneath your vehicle. This is normal.

- An air conditioner uses a lot of gas. Rather than always turning the air conditioner on, use the flow-through climate control setting.

- Switch on the air conditioner for a few minutes every week when the temperatures are above +10^{0}C (+50^0 F). Doing so circulates the refrigerant inside the hoses. Rubber seals around the hoses are also kept moist, preventing them from drying out and cracking, which can cause refrigerant leaks.

Climate Control Settings

- There are usually two climate control settings:
  1. Air Recirculation
     - ➤ Works with air already inside your vehicle.
     - ➤ Use when the air conditioner is turned on.
     - ➤ Use in the cold months, especially winter.
  2. Flow-Through
     - ➤ Allows outside air to replace air already inside your vehicle.
     - ➤ Prevents the inside windows from fogging.
     - ➤ Use in summer and on warm days.

Defroster and Heater Buttons

- Clear all interior ducts of obstructions so that they can adequately defrost the windows and keep your vehicle warm.
- Let the engine warm up for a couple of minutes before turning the defroster on as this prevents the engine from over exertion.
- Your vehicle should be warm inside and the windows defrosted, including the rear window, after the heater has been on for about five minutes.
- If the inside windows start to fog, put the defroster on high for a few minutes.
- In extremely cold temperatures, the defroster and heater can make a screeching sound when turned on. This may indicate the heater core or heater valve is defective. Or, it could be the parts are frozen and the sound should stop once the temperature rises.
- Overusing the rear defroster and side window demisters can cause the switches to malfunction.
- On most vehicles, the rear window defroster automatically turns off after approximately ten minutes.

Fuses

- Fuses, fusible links, and circuit breakers all serve the same purpose; to protect your vehicle's electrical system from overheating.

- The fuse box is usually located under the dashboard, close to the steering wheel. On some vehicles, a second fuse box sits under the hood.

- Inside the fuse box are all the fuses for the electrical components, such as air conditioner, brake lights, cigarette lighter, clock, dome light, heater, horn, meters, spare fuses, sunroof switch, turn-signal lights, and windshield wipers.

- Most fuse boxes are encased in a plastic cover. Inside the cover, labels should list what each fuse is for.

- Types of fuses include glass tube and spade.

- Most fuse boxes include a plastic fuse puller for removing a burnt fuse. Never remove a fuse with a screwdriver or other metal object as it can cause an electrical short.

- A burnt-out fuse is black, severed on its insides, or "cut" along its wiring.

- Most fuses are colour coded and rated. Always replace a blown fuse with one of the same colour and/or rating.

- Immediately replace a blown fuse with a new one so that the socket is not exposed to dust.

- If you are a smoker, one fuse that often "blows" is the cigarette lighter fuse (cigarette ashes get inside the lighter holder and cause a short).

- Fusible links are thin pieces of wire that are affixed along the wiring. An electrical surge can cause the wire to melt.

- Circuit breakers use a spring that snaps when a surge occurs.

JUST A SMOOTH AND EASY 100 K's

Gauges

Temperature Gauge

➤ Other than, or in addition to this gauge, an indicator light can turn red if there is a malfunction in the engine's temperature.

➤ If the gauge *slowly* moves towards the red zone, turn the heater or air conditioner on high. Stop your vehicle as soon as it is safe to do so.

➤ Immediately pull your vehicle over to the roadside and turn the ignition key off if the arrow *quickly* reaches the red zone.

Fuel Gauge

➤ Maintain the arrow on the fuel gauge between the one-half and full marks. Otherwise, air and water vapours can get into the fuel tank, causing the engine to stall.

➤ The fuel gauge often has a fuse as well as a sending unit, located in the fuel tank or on the engine block. A blown fuse or malfunctioning unit can cause an inaccurate reading on the fuel gauge.

Glove Compartment

What To Keep In The Glove Compartment

➤ A copy of *AutoTalk for Women*

➤ Your *vehicle owner's manual* (offers specific information about your automobile)

➤ A local *driver's licence handbook* (provides data on traffic control signs, right-of-ways, pavement markings, and other legalities pertaining to your province or state)

➤ Up-to-date city and provincial (state) highway *road maps*, along with Canadian and United States road maps

➤ *Office supplies,* such as a pencil, pencil sharpener, eraser, blank notepaper, small scissors, and a ruler (a pencil case easily holds these items)

➤ Small, working *flashlight*

➤ An old pair of *eyewear* (prescription glasses) if your driver's licence indicates correction lenses are required

What Not To Keep In The Glove Compartment

➤ Your vehicle *registration and insurance* (store these in a discrete location inside your trunk)

➤ Never leave your *name, address, and phone number* in the glove compartment (a safety feature)

➤ Never leave money, house keys, the garage door opener, or other *valuables* in the glove compartment (a safety feature)

➤ *Matches*, especially those in paper boxes, can ignite under the suffocating conditions inside a glove compartment

➤ *Medications* left in the glove box can get too hot, which may degrade or destroy their effectiveness

Hood Latch

• The lever for opening the hood is usually located below the dashboard, to the left of the driver's seat.

• Know the difference between the hood latch and the gas cover release latch.

• Ensure the hood is completely closed before driving.

• To prevent damage to the wiper blades, make sure they are down before releasing the hood latch.

Indicator Lights

• Indicator lights include the air bag, antilock brake, charge, emissions, engine, hazard, high beam, oil pressure, rear window defroster, right and left turn-signal arrows, and sunroof.

• On some manual transmission vehicles, a shift indicator light activates when it is most appropriate to shift gears.

• These lights are red (except for the right and left turn-signal arrows, which are green). The red light on each of the indicators should come on briefly when you start the engine. If the light stays on, see the section titled *Troubleshooting*.

Meters

Odometer

➤ This meter indicates the total number of kilometres (miles) your vehicle has travelled since it was manufactured.

➤ Although it is difficult to do, odometer readings can be tampered with.

Speedometer

➤ The speedometer indicates the speed at which your vehicle is moving.

➤ This meter is usually attached to a cable that can break.

Tachometer

➤ As an optional feature on some vehicles, the tachometer displays engine revolutions per minute.

➤ This meter is handy in manual transmission automobiles as it visibly indicates when to depress the clutch pedal.

Trip Odometer

➤ Set at zero, the trip odometer registers the total number of kilometres (miles) travelled during a particular trip.

Vehicle Identification Number (VIN)

• Your vehicle's unique identification number is affixed to a plate that is attached to the dashboard on the driver's side. This number is viewed through the outside of the front windshield. The VIN can also be located on the inside driver's door.

• The VIN is needed when obtaining vehicle registration and insurance.

• Keep your VIN in your wallet along with a colour photograph of your vehicle (make sure you can read the licence plate number in the photo). This information is beneficial to police if your vehicle is stolen (see *AutoTalk Assistant*).

Ventilation Outlets

• Before driving, make sure all the ventilation outlets are positioned where you want them and that they are free of obstructions.

• If driving in heavy traffic, close the outside vents. Move the climate control setting to air recirculation, rather than flow-through. This way, you won't be breathing in the exhaust fumes from other vehicles.

Doors and Locks

- Before driving, know where the buttons and knobs are on each of your vehicle doors.

- Always use the safety locks on all doors, especially the rear childproof locks.

- If the switches for the power door locks are constantly played with, the built-in protection circuit may activate, which prevents the power locks from working. Leave the system alone for a few minutes and the switches should readjust themselves.

- Always close a vehicle door when it's not in use. If the door stays open, the interior light stays on, which may cause the battery to discharge.

- Lubricate door hinges and locks to prevent corrosion and freezing. Lubricating also eliminates annoying squeaks.

- Keep drain holes in the doors free of obstructions. Without an escape route, water can enter the interior and stain the carpets.

- Periodically inspect the rubber stripping around door edges. Cracks in the rubber or missing rubber pieces prevents a tight seal around the door, which could also mean the door won't closely properly.

Floor and Floor Mats

- Floor mats reduce road and engine noises, as well as keeping the carpet and floor board clean.

- The driver's floor mat should be wide enough that it doesn't slide on the floor, but not so big to interfere with the gas, brake, and clutch pedals.

- Vacuum the vehicle floor every spring and fall to prevent mould and rust from occurring, especially underneath the floor mats.

- Using an automotive upholstery cleaner and a protective coating on the carpets makes it easier to keep them clean.

- Spills on the carpet and cloth floor mats can be quickly cleaned using soda water.

- Think about investing in winter floor mats. Removing salt stains from carpets is difficult.

- Wash rubber floor mats with a brush using soapy water. Rinse them well. Be sure they are completely dry before placing them back in your vehicle.

- An open container of baking soda placed under a front seat helps absorb interior odours, such as food and tobacco.

Parking Brake

- The parking brake prevents your vehicle from moving when it is parked by applying shoes, or pads, against the rear wheels. Its job is not to stop your vehicle suddenly. Calling it the emergency brake is; therefore, a misnomer.

- When applying the parking brake, the brakes should be dry. Wet brakes often stick, resulting in an ineffective parking brake.

- To prevent damage to the brake system, fully disengage the parking brake before driving.

- If your vehicle is parked outside in temperatures below –10°C (+14°F), the parking brake cable may freeze and snap if it is used.

- The parking brake cable, located underneath your vehicle, stretches over time. To adjust the cable, start by pulling up and clicking once on the parking brake lever. Adjust the screw on the cable so that the shoes, or pads, just start to put pressure on the rear wheels. Be careful not to over-tighten the cable, as added pressure can cause it to break.

- Your vehicle should not move when the parking brake is applied. If you can drive your vehicle with the parking brake still engaged, the cable is probably loose or broken.

Pedals - Brake, Clutch, and Gas

Brake Pedal

- Always put a foot on the brake pedal when turning the ignition on.
- When driving, only use your right foot on the brake pedal. This prevents you from "riding the brakes." Keeping your left foot on the brake pedal while using your right foot on the gas pedal can cause brake damage, poor gas mileage, or the brakes can stop working altogether. "Riding the brakes" also confuses drivers behind you as every time your foot touches the brake pedal, the brake lights are activated.
- There are situations when it is advantageous to keep your right foot on top of the brake pedal without actually depressing it (make sure the brake lights don't go on). Coming to a red or yellow traffic light or anticipating another stop are examples when that extra second or two of timing needed to brake may help you avoid a collision.
- Use the toes (all of the toes, not just their tips) of your right foot to brake. Keep the heel of your right foot on the floor. Why? Placing your whole foot on the brake pedal means using your thigh muscles. These muscles cannot maintain the finer movement control needed to brake. Using the small muscles in your foot and ankle gives you the flexibility necessary to brake quickly and safely.

WHOA, THERE GIRL ....EASY NOW...
BRAKE FIRM AND STEADY. "WHEW".
THANK GOODNESS FOR ANTI-LOCK BRAKES

- Antilock brakes are standard on most vehicles today, although they vary in sound and feel on the brake pedal. For example, antilock brakes can result in some vibration on the brake pedal. Become familiar with the antilock braking characteristics on your vehicle. Test the brakes in an empty parking lot. How does the brake pedal feel? What sounds do you hear coming from the brakes? How does your vehicle move when the brakes are applied?

- Brake pedal extenders enable drivers 163 cm (5 ft. 4 in.) and under to sit farther from the steering wheel (a minimum of 25 to 30 cm [10 to 12 in.] from the steering wheel to your chest is recommended). The extenders are universal, so ensure one is properly fitted onto the brake pedal by a reputable installer. Once fitted, the extender is permanent.

Clutch Pedal

- The clutch pedal should move approximately 1.9 to 2.5 cm ($^3/_4$ to 1 in.) without effort and then reach the floor with a heavy push of your left foot.

- It is important to get a feel for the friction point on the clutch pedal (the point when the clutch pedal is slowly released and the gas pedal applied), so that a smooth shifting of gears results. A tachometer, or the shift indicator light, visually displays when the clutch pedal should be engaged or released.

- When starting a vehicle with a manual transmission, make sure the clutch pedal is fully depressed.

- "Riding the clutch" (keeping your left foot on the clutch pedal while accelerating or braking) can wear down parts in the clutch system.

Gas Pedal

- The gas pedal is also referred to as the accelerator.

- Always use your right foot on the gas pedal.

- Use your toes to depress the gas pedal. Keep the heel of your right foot on the floor so that you can pivot to the brake pedal with ease. By using this "heel and toe" method, you use the small muscles in your foot and ankle, which gives you greater control over the gas and brake pedals.

- Gas pedal extenders enable drivers 163 cm (5 ft. 4 in.) and under to sit farther from the steering wheel (a minimum of 25 to 30 cm [10 to 12 in.] from the steering wheel to your chest is recommended). The extenders are universal, so ensure one is properly fitted onto the gas pedal by a reputable installer. Once fitted, the extender is permanent.

- You should not have to depress the gas pedal when starting the engine of a fuel-injected vehicle. In very cold temperatures, though, you need to be careful not to flood the engine if you pump the gas pedal.

- Start a vehicle with a carburetor with the gas pedal depressed halfway down. Keep in mind, though, vehicles with carburetors can easily flood.

Rear-View Mirror

- Most rear-view mirrors have a dipper switch for day vs. night driving.

- Some mirrors "self-dim," depending on the amount of light reflected from behind your vehicle.

- Adjust the rear-view mirror only after the driver's seat is correctly positioned and before driving.

- If you cannot see out of the rear-view mirror, driver *and* passenger-side view mirrors must be attached to your vehicle.

- If you need to secure the rear-view mirror to the front windshield, special adhesive bonding (available at most automotive stores) can be used to glue the mirror to the centre of the window.

Seat Belts

The Safety on Seat Belts

- Seat belts hold you, the driver, and each occupant down (lap belt) and back (shoulder belt) against the seat. They protect you and your passengers in the event of a collision or rollover. Wearing lap and shoulder belts also help you stay in control of your vehicle, especially in emergency situations.

- Some vehicles won't start if the seat belt is not buckled.

- Seat belts should not be twisted when worn. They should also be clean, dry, and have no frays.

- Dirt, food particles, and other grime often become lodged in the seat belt buckles, which can cause the buckles to malfunction.

- To be effective, buckles and retractors on all seat belts must have their respective bolts tightly attached to the belts.

- Seat belt units usually cannot be repaired; they must be replaced.

Adults Using Seat Belts

- Seat belts must be worn at all times while your vehicle is moving forward. This includes driving in shopping malls, on all city streets and rural roads, and on highways.

- Traffic violations include the improper use of seat belts, for the driver and all passengers.

- Seat belts provide ideal restraint when you are seated straight or with a slight tilt, rather than in a reclining position. Sitting relatively straight also reduces back fatigue.

WHEN YOU LOVE SOMEBODY

- Fit the shoulder belt across your collarbone and over your chest. Never place the shoulder belt under your arm as your chest and ribs are exposed to serious injury. Secure the lap belt across your hips, not over your waist or lower abdomen. Yank on both belts to ensure a tight fit.

- Shoulder belts can loosen while you are driving. Make sure the shoulder belt always provides a snug fit across your chest by periodically extending the strap and then quickly releasing it.

- There are as many seat belt systems as there are makes of vehicles. This is especially important to remember when purchasing a new or used vehicle. Since seat belts are worn every time you get behind the wheel, be comfortable with their fit.

- Emergency locking retractors (ELR) are equipped on some vehicles. Also called "pre-tensioner seat belts" or "crash tensioners," these belts automatically tighten when a sudden stop or collision occurs. Their advantage is that your body does not jerk forward during this abrupt movement, which is especially important if the air bag is deployed.

- Many automotive manufacturers are installing height-adjustable shoulder belt anchors attached to the centre pillar of vehicles. These shoulder belts offer the convenience of having the strap fit safely and comfortably across your collarbone and chest regardless of your height.

- Some vehicles are equipped with a rear-centre lap belt. Use this seat belt if transporting more than two passengers in the back seat of your vehicle.

- If you are pregnant, it is imperative you still wear your shoulder belt and that your lap belt fits snuggly below your belly. Limit your driving time during the last three months of pregnancy as your baby is too close to the steering wheel.

- A seat belt pad or adjuster offers additional comfort across your collarbone and chest.

Transporting Children

Legalities

> Children learn through imitation. By always wearing your seat belt, you teach family members the importance of buckling up.

> Children may not have the know-how to safely put their seat belts on. Make it a habit to buckle up your children or always check that they correctly strap themselves in the rear seat.

➤ Instruct family members to never unbuckle their seat belt while they are inside a moving vehicle. Make this a "no exception" rule.

➤ The law dictates that all children travelling inside your vehicle must be properly secured in a government-approved child-restraint seat or buckled in a seat belt. It is illegal to hold a child in your lap while your vehicle is moving.

➤ Infant carriers and other child-restraint seats require government certification. This SOC (statement of compliance) label must be affixed to each carrier and restraint seat. The label should also include the manufacturer's name, the name and model number of the seat, the date it was manufactured, instructions for installation (each make and model has specific procedures to follow), and weight and height restrictions.

➤ Canadian standards differ from United States regulations with regards to child-restraint seats. For example, in the U.S., tether straps are not mandatory on forward-facing child-restraint seats. In Canada, you can be ticketed if your child-restraint seat does not meet CMVSS (Canadian Motor Vehicle Safety Standards) set by Transport Canada, which includes having, and correctly using, the tether strap on a forward-facing child-restraint seat.

➤ Some insurance companies will not pay medical bills if a child was injured during a collision in which a child-restraint seat was not used. This also holds true if the child-restraint seat was not installed according to the manufacturer's and vehicle's specifications.

➤ Some vehicles have door-mounted seat belts. Child-restraint seats cannot be used with these seat belts. To accommodate a restraint seat in such a vehicle, have a floor-mounted seat belt professionally installed.

Types of Child-Restraint Seats

➤ There are five types of manufactured child-restraint seats:

1. Infant Carriers

■ These seats are suited for infants weighing up to 9 kg (20 lb.) and measuring up to 66 cm (26 in.) in length.

■ Infant carriers are well-suited for premature and low birth weight babies.

■ Baby beds are illegal child-restraint seats. Always look for the government-approved statement of compliance label on the infant carrier.

■ Once your infant is in the carrier, click the strap buckle in its slot. Then adjust the shoulder harness, making sure the straps lie flat across the front of your infant. Use a chest retainer clip to keep the harness straps safely over the shoulders. Adjust the clip so that it is level with your baby's armpits. You can also add a second clip to help hold the straps in their proper place. And, one more safety point here – there should be only one finger between the harness and your baby's chest.

■ Always place the infant carrier in the back seat of your vehicle. The middle of the back seat is the safest place, rather than on one side as your baby is likely to be farthest away from any impact, especially in a side collision.

■ An infant carrier must face the rear of your vehicle. This means that once your infant is secured in the carrier and it is strapped in the back seat, she or he faces the vehicle's trunk.

■ Never place an infant carrier in a front passenger seat equipped with an air bag in the dashboard.

■ An infant carrier, once installed using the vehicle's seat belts, can move forward and back slightly, but it should never move from side to side.

■ For maximum safety, recline the infant carrier to no more than a 45° angle. If the slope of your vehicle's back seat causes the carrier to recline too much, use a tightly rolled towel at the crease of the backseat, under the carrier, to correct the angle.

■ Once your infant is strapped in the carrier and it is secured in the back seat, lock the carrying handle into position at the back of the carrier, even if it is equipped with sunshades.

■ Once your infant is correctly secured in the carrier in the back seat, cover her or him with a blanket. It is safer to drape the blanket over the harness straps, rather than placing the blanket between your infant and the straps.

2. Combination (Convertible) Seats

➤ As combination seats are used both rear- and forward-facing, they are suited for infants and toddlers.

a) Rear-Facing Combination Seats

■ This position suits infants weighing up to 9 kg (20 lb.) and measuring up to 66 cm (26 in.) in length.

■ Combination seats have various types of restraining devices: an abdominal shield, an arm bar, a five-point harness, or a retractable harness.

■ Slide the harness straps on the restraint seat into the lowest slot, which should be at or below your infant's ears. When threading the strap through the metal slide, adjust the straps one at a time so that you can use the other strap as an example of how to correctly thread it. Make sure the straps are doubled back for added strength.

■ Place the combination seat in the back seat so that your infant faces the rear of your vehicle. The seat should be secured using your vehicle's seat belts. As the tether strap is not used, tie this strap so that it doesn't flop around.

■ Once your infant is in the restraint seat, click the strap buckle in its slot. If the restraint seat has straps, adjust the straps so that they lie flat across the front of your infant. Use a chest retainer clip to keep the harness straps safely over the shoulders. Adjust the clip so that it is level with your baby's armpits. You can also add a second clip to help hold the straps in their proper place. And, one more safety point here – there should be only one finger between the bar, shield, or straps and your baby's chest.

b) Forward-Facing Combination Seats

■ These seats are suited for toddlers weighing 9 to 22 kg (20 to 48 lb.).

■ Some combination seats have a weight limit of 18 kg (40 lb.) and a height of 101 cm (40 in.).

■ The straps on the combination seat should be at your toddler's shoulders or slightly above or below them. Make sure you thread each strap through the metal slide for firm support. Adjust the straps one at a time so that you can use the other one as an example of how to correctly thread it. Make sure the straps are doubled back for added strength.

■ Use your vehicle's seat belts to secure the combination seat so that it faces forward. There should be little movement of the restraint seat once it is strapped in the back seat.

■ Forward-facing combination seats should always be in as much an upright position as possible for maximum safety.

■ To meet with CMVSS, each combination seat must have a tether strap made of sturdy seat belt material. When installing the combination seat front-facing, it is mandatory to use the tether strap. This strap keeps the seat top secured in the event of a sudden stop or collision. The tether strap also helps limit the seat's side to side movement.

■ Secure the tether strap to a hook that must be anchored to a solid metal part at the back of your vehicle. Most vehicles built today have a pre-installed hook.

■ The tether strap should be anchored so that it sits at no more than a 20° angle to either side of the restraint seat. Ideally, the strap should fit straight back.

■ Once your toddler is in the restraint seat, click the strap buckle in its slot. If the restraint seat has straps, adjust the straps so that they lie flat across the front of your child. Use a chest retainer clip to keep the harness straps safely over the shoulders. Adjust the clip so that it is level with your child's armpits. You can also add a second clip to help hold the straps in their proper place. And, one more safety point here – there should be only one finger between the bar, shield, or straps and your toddler's chest.

3. Booster Seats (Cushions)

➤ Booster seats are suited for children weighing between 18 and 27 kg (40 to 60 lb.).

➤ A booster seat raises your child so that the shoulder and lap belts fit safely and securely across her or his chest and hips. It is for this reason that a booster seat is safer than using only the seat belt.

➤ Children too big for booster cushions must wear seat belts. Make sure the shoulder belt fits across your child's chest so as not to obstruct her or his neck. Never place the shoulder belt under your child's arm. The lap belt must fit snugly across the hips, not over the stomach. Keep in mind that shoulder and lap belts are designed for adult bodies.

➤ There are three types of booster seats. Choose a booster cushion that best fits the seat belt system in your vehicle.

  a) In vehicles having shoulder and lap belts, select a booster seat that safely and comfortably positions these seat belts on your child.

  b) Some minivans and other vehicles have low back seats. Purchase a booster seat with a high back, to protect your child's head and neck.

  c) If your vehicle has only lap belts, your child must still be secured across the chest. Choose a booster seat with a shield that fits over your child's chest.

4. Built-In Child-Restraint Seats

➤ These seats are either forward-facing child-restraint seats or booster cushions built into the back bench seats of vehicles.

➤ These seats are designed for children weighing between 9 and 27 kg (20 to 60 lb.) and who are over one year of age.

➤ Built-in restraint seats must also meet government standards and require certification.

➤ A tether strap is not required on built-in restraint seats.

5. Handicapped Child-Restraint Seats

➤ Most of these restraint seats fit children weighing between 9 and 36 kg (20 to 80 lb.).

➤ Specially designed restraint seats provide safe and secure transportation for children with cerebral palsy, epilepsy, spina bifida, and other special needs.

Where to Put the Kids

➤ Keep all children safely secured in the rear seat of your vehicle using a government-approved child-restraint seat, booster seat, or in a seat belt.

➤ The middle of the back seat is the safest place for your child, rather than on one side.

➤ Never place a child-restraint seat in the front passenger seat that has an air bag inside the dashboard.

➤ Think of where to put the kids this way - the front seating area remains an "adult only territory" while the rear seat is for "kids only."

Purchasing and Installing Child-Restraint Seats

➤ The middle of the back seat is the safest place for your child, rather than on one side.

➤ If you live in Canada, only purchase a child-restraint seat meeting CMVSS set by Transport Canada. Always look for this government-approved statement of compliance label affixed to the side, back, or bottom of the restraint seat.

➤ By mailing in the registration card that comes with the new restraint seat, you will be informed of any recalls on the seat.

➤ Never use a child-restraint seat that is more than 10 years old although some manufacturers have a lower age restriction.

➤ Second-hand child-restraint seats require careful scrutiny. Look for the government-approved label and check for rust, cracks, and frayed straps on the restraint seat. Is the manufacturer's instruction manual available? It should be. Check if that particular model has been recalled.

➤ Never purchase or utilize a child-restraint seat if it has been dropped or involved in a collision. If your vehicle has been in a collision and the child-restraint seat was in the vehicle, remove the tether strap and harness system, tear out the padding, and do whatever is necessary to make sure that it can never be used again. Often, a discarded child-restraint seat will be picked up and re-used. In most cases, your vehicle's insurance policy covers the replacement of the child-restraint seat if it was in a vehicle involved in a collision.

➤ Comfort and ease of use are two important factors when buying a child-restraint seat. Bring your infant or toddler along with you when purchasing the seat so that she or he can sit in several models. Remember that your child wears heavier clothing in colder months, so ensure the child-restraint seat can accommodate the added bulk, but also keep your child secured in the seat.

➤ Test child-restraint seats before purchasing. Install the seat on the back seat of your vehicle to ensure a safe and snug fit using the seat belts. Make sure the restraint seat base doesn't extend too far over the back seat.

➤ Always install a child-restraint seat according to the manufacturer's instructions *and* to your vehicle's specifications.

➤ When installing a child-restraint seat, check for safe degree of seat tilt. Reclining the seat too much could force your child to eject from the seat if a collision occurs.

➤ When tightening the seat belts across the child-restraint seat, push down on the seat with your knee. Move the seat in all directions to ensure a secure position.

➤ A locking clip is a small, "H" shaped, metal device used to keep the seat belts properly positioned and tight (it hooks over your vehicle's shoulder and lap belts once they have been used to secure the restraint seat). Install the clip so that there is no more than 1.3 cm ($1/_2$ in.) between the clip and the slot attachment on the seat belt. Even if your rear seat belts have automatic locking retractors (ALR), install the locking clip. You can never give too much protection for your child.

➤ To comply with Canadian standards, a forward-facing child-restraint seat must have a tether strap extend from the back of the seat and be secured to a hook anchored to a solid metal part at the back of your vehicle. Most new vehicles have a built-in tether hook. If your vehicle does not have one, a dealership can install one. Or, check service stations as some offer complimentary installation when you provide the hook.

➤ Never use the anchor hook for two child-restraint seats.

➤ Are you a two-vehicle family? Install an anchor hook in the second vehicle so that you can readily move the child-restraint seat from one back seat to the other.

➤ Your local health unit usually has a staff member who can inspect an installed child-restraint seat. She or he can inform you if the restraint seat meets government standards and if it is properly fitted in your vehicle.

➤ Before placing your child in the restraint seat, make sure there are no hot metal parts on the restraint seat or that it is "too cold for comfort."

➤ Secure boxes, bags, and other items in the back of your minivan, hatchback, or station wagon when your child is sitting in the rear seat. A sudden stop can cause loose items to fall forward and harm your child.

➤ Canada and the United States are negotiating a universal installation procedure for child-restraint seats. Called Canfix (Canada) and Isofix (United States), the child-restraint seat utilizes a three-point design. The forecasted date for this implementation is 2002.

Seats and Head Restraints

Seats

- Bench, bucket, or captain's chair seats are installed based on an average height and weight. What the seats are made of also affects driver and passenger comfort.

- When you are seated, your eye level should be well above the steering wheel. Use a firm cushion if necessary, but make sure it doesn't slide back and forth while you drive.

- For safety reasons, position the driver and front passenger seats as far back from the dashboard as possible. The recommended minimum distance between the driver and steering wheel, and the front passenger and dashboard, is 25 to 30 cm (10 to 12 in.).

- Ensure the driver's seat is locked into position after any seat adjustments have been by trying to move the seat forward and backward using your body weight.

- To minimize risk of injury in a collision, the driver and all passengers should have their seats in an upright position (or with only a slight recline).

- Putting feet on the dashboard while the vehicle is moving is a safety hazard, especially if the front passenger seat has an air bag in the dashboard.

- Some vehicles are equipped with heated seats. Be aware that driving for any length of time in a heated seat can make you drowsy.

- Some automobile manufacturers are installing side air bags inside the seat's backrest. In a collision, sensors along the door's side-impact beam deploy this air bag to the side of you, along the door. At the time of publication, there are no statistics regarding the effect these air bags have on drivers or passengers.

- Vacuum the front and rear seats when vacuuming the floor and floor mats every spring and fall.

- If your seats have covers, periodically remove them and laundry or professionally clean the covers.

- Using a stain repellent on cloth seats reduces the risk of permanent spots.

- Spills on cloth seats can be quickly cleaned using soda water.

- Fight the odour of sour milk with a paste of baking soda and water. You can also use baking soda and vinegar or vinegar and water. Wipe the area dry after washing it.

- Repair seat tears using strong thread or a specialized patch kit.
- Consider investing in a carbon monoxide detector and fire extinguisher for your vehicle. Secure them under one of the seats.

Head Restraints

- Head restraints are just that – they help reduce head and neck (whiplash) injuries when a collision occurs. They are not for resting your head.
- Adjust the head restraints so that the middle or top of the driver's and passenger's ears is even with the centre of the restraint.
- Each head restraint should also sit directly behind the back of the driver's and passenger's head. Called "backset," there should be less than 5 cm (2 in.) of space between the back of the occupant's head and the front of the head restraint.
- Make sure the head restraint is locked into position after it has been adjusted. Some head restraints do not securely latch, which means they can easily move up or down if a collision occurs.
- Once the head restraint is positioned, look in the rear-view mirror. You should be able to see clearly out the back window. Is the restraint blocking your view? If so, readjust the driver's seat and ensure your vehicle has two side-view mirrors.

Steering Wheel

Air Bag

- Automobile manufacturers are now equipping vehicles with an air bag stowed inside the hub of the steering wheel.
- Effective air bags deploy in high speed front-end collisions, although they can inflate during low speed crashes.
- The heights of the driver and front passenger affect the reliability of air bags. Shorter women (142 to 163 cm [4 ft. 8 in. to 5 ft. 4 in.]) are especially vulnerable to the high speed at which air bags are deployed, even when seat belts are used.
- Statistics indicate air bags reduce fatalities, but most automotive manufacturers have issued warnings about the potential dangers of air bags. Watch for these notices in letters, a label on the sun visor, or in the owner's manual.
- A deployed air bag must be professionally replaced.

- An exploding air bag has a popping sound. Smoke that is sometimes seen with a deflated air bag is talc or starch from inside the air bag.
- On-off switches for passenger-side air bags are installed on some vehicles, but no on-off switches are or will be installed for driver-side air bags.
- To reduce fatalities caused by air bags, automobile manufacturers are now installing dual-speed air bags on some vehicles. These air bags deploy with 20 to 35% less force than the one-speed air bags, which deploy at 330 km/h (200 mph).

Cruise Control

- Before driving, be familiar with the cruise control settings, including how to cancel it.
- Ideally, set the cruise control at approximately 1 km/h (1 mph) below your desired speed.
- It is never safe to use the cruise control when driving in heavy traffic that constantly varies its speed, on winding roads, on ice- or snow-covered roads, on hills, or during adverse weather conditions.

High- and Low-Beam Switch

- Some vehicles are equipped with daytime running lights (DRL), which automatically activate when the ignition is turned on. This alleviates using the low beams during daylight hours.
- Know what is required by law as to when to stop using DRL and switch on the low beams. For example, you must drive from one hour before dusk to one hour after dawn using low beams, but the exact times vary depending on the time of year.
- Use low beams (or fog lights, if your vehicle is equipped with them) when driving in fog. Never use the parking lights, as they do not provide sufficient visibility for other motorists.
- On most vehicles, a blue coloured light on the dashboard indicates when the high beams are on.
- High beams work well when driving on highways and rural roads. Switch to low beams for oncoming traffic and when a vehicle is passing you.

GETTIN' DARK,
TIME TO BRIGHTEN
UP THE ROAD.
LOW BEAMS, OF
COURSE!

Horn

- Your vehicle must have a working horn. However, use it sparingly.

- Periodically test the horn to be sure it works and does not stick.

- Some horn switches are mounted inside the steering wheel. These switches can become defective.

- If the horn sticks, pull the horn fuse or disconnect the negative battery cable.

Ignition Switch

- The ignition switch has four functions: Off (lock), ACC (accessories), Start (to start the engine), and On (after the engine has started).

- Most ignition keys have an identification number embossed on them. This number is required when duplicating keys. Memorize this number or write it down and keep it in your wallet (see *AutoTalk Assistant*).

- If your vehicle has an anti-theft system, the ignition key may contain a computer chip. The key, once inserted in the ignition, sends a signal to the engine confirming the code. Making replacements for these types of keys is expensive, as the key must be programmed to your particular vehicle code. Alleviate this expense by asking the sales associate to give you an extra ignition key when you purchase a new vehicle.

- A heavy key chain, or one that has lots of keys, weighs down the ignition key when it sits in the ignition switch. Eventually, the key bends and can break while it is in the ignition switch.

- Release the ignition key as soon as the engine starts or the starter system can become damaged.

- The ignition switch does not affect some electrical circuits, such as the radio memory system. If your vehicle will not be driven for awhile, disengage the battery cables so that these electrical circuits do not drain the battery, causing it to discharge.

Right and Left Turn-Signal Arm

- Engage the right or left turn-signal arm when making a turn, changing lanes, or pulling over to the side of the road.

- The right and left turn-signal arm activates the green arrow indicator lights, causing them to flash. The signal arm also sets the front and rear signal lights flashing.

I LIKE EVERYBODY TO KNOW WHERE I'M COMING FROM, OR, IN THIS CASE, WHERE I'M GOING !!

- The green arrow on the indicator light and the signal lights at the front and rear of your vehicle should stop flashing once the turn or lane change is completed.

- The signal arm should disengage once the steering wheel returns to a straight position.

Steering Wheel

- To maintain control of the steering wheel (and your vehicle) always keep both hands on the wheel.

- Automobile manufacturers are now equipping the steering wheel with an air bag.

- For the air bag to be effective, maintain a minimum distance of 25 to 30 cm (10 to12 in.) between the steering wheel and your chest.

- If your vehicle is equipped with tilt on the steering wheel, tilt it slightly down, towards your chest so that, if the air bag deploys, it won't hit your neck and face with full force.

- Your arms are most comfortable when they are at a 45° angle to the steering wheel. Never wrap your thumbs around the steering wheel, but do place your hands at the 9:00 and 3:00 positions, rather than at 10:00 and 2:00. This could prevent your wrists or arms from breaking, or reduce soft tissue injury to your arms, hands, or upper body if the air bag is deployed.

- The steering wheel may house controls, such as the audio and climate control settings. Even though this location is convenient, you should become familiar with these controls prior to driving.

- "Dry steering" (turning the steering wheel when your vehicle is stopped) can damage the steering column.

- With the ignition turned to "on" (not "start"), slowly turn the steering wheel from side to side. More than 1.3 cm ($^1/_2$ in.) of play on the steering wheel before the front wheels turn often indicates defective steering components.

- Rack-and-pinion steering, standard on most vehicles, consists of a "rack of gears" along a long rod, a shaft that extends from the steering wheel to this rack, and tie rods and steering arms that are attached to the long rod and wheels. If the unit starts leaking, the entire unit must be replaced, not just the individual part. The rubber seals at the tie rods can also dry out and crack, making it difficult to move the steering wheel.

Wiper Blades Switch

- The wiper blades *switch* is linked to a motor that is often protected by a fuse located in the fuse box. The wiper blades *motor* is usually located near the cowl under the hood (close to the front windshield), or it may be located under the dashboard (near the glove compartment).

- The switch for activating the front wiper blades is usually located on an arm extending from the steering wheel. The rear wiper blade switch is most often situated on the dashboard.

- A wiper blade fuse can "blow" in winter as a result of using the wiper switch when the blades are frozen to the windshield.

- The wiper blades switch should operate quietly. If you hear a noise other than the usual sound of the blades in motion, there may be a defect within the switch or the motor may need to be replaced.

- Most vehicles built today include a multi-speed wiper motor. This allows you to vary wiper speeds according to the amount of precipitation.

Technology in Vehicles

Recent innovations in the automotive industry have added a number of conveniences and safety features to vehicles. Examples of these new accessories include:

Air Bags

- "Smart" air bags are computer-sensored air bags that deploy depending on the weight or position of the occupant.

- "Dual-threshold" air bags, another sensored-driven feature, determine if the occupant is wearing a seat belt. The speed at which the air bag is deployed depends on whether the sensor indicates the seat belt is used.

- Air bags for the knees, legs, and feet deploy from the carpet. They work to reduce lower leg injuries.

- An inflatable curtain air bag drops from the ceiling to cover the entire length and width of the vehicle. This protects the heads of the driver and passenger and prevents anyone being thrown from the vehicle.

Audio Visual Systems

- A small television, hooked to a VCR, extends from the vehicle's ceiling. Back-seat occupants can then watch their favourite program or video.

- A radio and CD player are also part of the back-seat system in which sounds reach the rear speakers only. Front-seat occupants then have the option of listening to the same music or "tuning-out" completely.

- A special antenna keeps motorists within reach of their favourite radio station, no matter where they are.

Black Box

- Similar to an airplane black box, a vehicle's black box records and transmits data to reveal details of a collision, such as the speed at which the vehicle was travelling.

Braking Sensors

- Without the driver having to put one foot on the brake pedal, sensors automatically stop the vehicle, which is advantageous if a sudden stop is necessary.

Computer

- A small computer acts as a mobile gadget for wireless communication. Through voice commands, the driver can access e-mail or the Internet, switch radio stations, and make telephone calls.

- A passenger seat desktop computer with a compartment for a printer and file folders is another recent innovation. Read the manufacturer's label and this feature is put into perspective – "Use only when parked."

Cruise Control

- Adaptive cruise control uses laser radar (or infrared sensors) to monitor traffic. For example, if the vehicle in front of you speeds up, your vehicle automatically increases its speed.

Glass Divider

- A glass divider (like the ones in cabs, limousines, and police cars) fits between the front and rear seats of a vehicle. Noises in the back seat are muffled, offering a quiet ride for front-seat occupants.

Head Restraints

- "Active" head restraints help reduce head and neck injuries. These padded pressure plates activate based on how much force the driver's and passenger's head and neck hit the restraints.

Motion Screens

- One such small screen fits into the front windshield. Its sensors monitor movement and images, which is beneficial during night driving when vision is reduced.

- Another type of screen uses radar sensors situated at both the front and rear of the vehicle. These sensors scan for objects so that collisions can be avoided.

Navigation System

- A dashboard-mounted, computer driven system enables the driver to input her or his destination. Linked to orbiting satellites, the computer displays the desired route.

- Through this system, the driver can also access security and conveniences, such as the closest banking machine, police station, hospital, and hotel.

- Tracking capabilities in some navigation systems lets others know of the whereabouts of the vehicle. Used in emergency situations, the driver activates a telephone keypad and an operator quickly dispatches an ambulance or tow truck. Taking this one step further, another sensor detects unusual changes in the vehicle's movement and automatically dials help; an advantage if the driver is unconscious.

Transmission Settings and Gears

Automatic Transmission Settings

- When driving, keep your hand off the automatic shift lever so that you don't inadvertently shift gears while your vehicle is moving.

- An automatic transmission usually has six settings with an optional overdrive (D) setting:

P = Parking

➤ Most engines having an automatic transmission are started in "P."

➤ Always park in "P," especially when parking up- or downhill.

➤ Make sure your vehicle does not move when parked by engaging the parking brake after the gear is placed in "P."

➤ When shifting from "P" into "D" or "R," always keep your right foot on the brake pedal.

R = Reverse

➤ This gear is used when backing up your vehicle.

➤ The engine will not start in "R."

➤ Make sure your vehicle is fully stopped before putting the gear in "R," or transmission failure can result.

➤ Some vehicles make a noise once the gear is put in "R" to let other motorists and pedestrians hear your intention to back up.

➤ On some vehicles, a reverse sensing device warns if objects are hidden at the back of the vehicle when it is put into "R."

N = Neutral

➤ A vehicle can be parked and sometimes started in "N," but it is safer to park and start the engine in "P."

➤ A vehicle can periodically be shifted into "N" when the engine is idling roughly and threatening to stall, especially in heavy stop-and-go traffic.

➤ Never coast downhill in "N" as the brakes can overheat.

D = Drive

➤ "D" is used in normal driving conditions.

➤ The engine will not start when in "D."

1 = Low Gear

➤ This gear increases power while driving at a low speed.

➤ Use "1" when going up steep hills or for maximum braking when driving down steep hills.

➤ When driving through sand or mud, "1" is the ideal setting.

➤ Do not use this gear when driving faster than 65 km/h (40 mph). Check your vehicle owner's manual for the maximum speed limit when driving in "1."

2 = Second Gear

➤ This gear is used when driving at a higher speed using less power.

➤ "2" can also be used when driving slowly in heavy stop-and-go traffic.

➤ Shifting to "2" gives your vehicle extra power when driving on soft roads.

➤ Do not use this gear at speeds faster than 120 km/h (75 mph). Check your vehicle owner's manual for the maximum speed limit when driving in "2."

D = Overdrive (Optional)

➤ This gear means the transmission has two drive ranges: "D" (normal) and "D" (overdrive transmission).

➤ Usually, there is a button that pushes in and out to indicate the drive range.

➤ Overdrive decreases engine speed, but your vehicle speed stays the same as in "D" (normal), which reduces fuel consumption and engine wear.

➤ This gear is ideal when driving at highway speeds or up a long hill.

Manual Transmission Gears

• A manual transmission usually has four or five forward speeds (along with "R" and "N"), arranged in an "H" shifting pattern, and having the following functions:

R = Reverse

➤ This gear is used to back up your vehicle.

➤ You can park in "R," but it is more practical to park in "1."

N = Neutral

➤ "N" can be used when starting the engine.

➤ This gear is periodically used when the engine is idling, such as in heavy stop-and-go traffic.

➤ Do not park in "N" as your vehicle can roll.

1 - First (Low) Gear

➤ This gear is used to slowly start moving your vehicle

➤ "1" can be used for parking your vehicle. A manual transmission vehicle can be started in "1" so parking in this gear alleviates changing to another gear after starting the engine.

➤ When at red lights and stop signs, leave the gear in "1," rather than shifting to "N." In "1," you can move your vehicle more quickly if, for example, it looks like someone is going to rear-end you. Also, you are not apt to roll back once you start moving your vehicle from a stopped position.

2 - Second Gear

➤ Use this gear for accelerating your vehicle.

3 – Third (High) Gear

➤ This gear is used when driving at highway speeds under normal weather and road conditions.

4 – Fourth and Fifth Gears

➤ Use this gear for maximum fuel benefits.

➤ These gears work on the same premise as the overdrive gear in automatics.

➤ Overdrive decreases engine speed, but your vehicle speed stays the same, which reduces fuel consumption and engine wear.

➤ Ideally, use this gear for when driving at highway speeds or up a long hill.

Windows

- Your vehicle insurance may not cover glass if the front windshield is cracked or chipped. Decide which makes more sense economically - replacing the glass and obtaining glass coverage or having insurance with no glass coverage.

- Cracks, breaks, and discoloration in the front, rear, and side windows are safety hazards for visibility.

- Cracked or torn weather stripping along the side windows often results in rust along these areas. It also lets cold air seep into the interior of your vehicle.

- When using the power window switch, make sure no passengers have their fingers or hands on the window ledge. This includes the sunroof.

- Constant playing with the power window switch can cause windows to jam.

- Keep windows closed when driving at high speeds to reduce wind drag. Use the vents for air circulation.

- Never try to open windows if they are frozen shut.

- If the interior windows start to fog, put the defroster on high for a few minutes, position the climate control setting to flow-through, open a side window or vent, or turn the air conditioner on.

- Never leave loose objects on the back windowsill. They can seriously harm the driver or any passengers if a sudden stop or collision occurs.

- Dirt and smoke produce a thin film on the interior of windows that affects visibility. Periodically wash all windows on the inside, including the sunroof, using a mixture of vinegar and water.

- To help protect windows from fogging, especially in winter, clean the inside of the windows with an ammonia-based window cleaner before the cold weather starts.

- Abrasive cleaners can damage rear defogger grids. Use a soft, clean cloth to wipe the rear window.

Section 2
Exterior of Your Vehicle

The exterior of your vehicle includes the body, mirrors, lights, tires, and windows. These parts are easily recognizable and show obvious signs of damage or that they are wearing out. Accessories, such as roof and trunk racks, can equip your vehicle with bikes, boats, and skis. Tools and other supplies in the trunk make for handy items needed when necessary.

For specific information on the exterior features of your car or multi-purpose vehicle (minivan, light truck, or sport-utility vehicle), consult the owner's manual.

SECTION TWO CONTENTS

...cont'd

Introduction

A clean vehicle makes it, and you, more visible on the road. Keeping the lights and wiper blades in good condition and windows clean also improves your ability to see while behind the wheel.

Tires are what hold you and your car or multi-purpose vehicle to the pavement. It's imperative each tire can handle high intensity heat and lots of weight. Do you have any tools in the trunk and, if so, are they compatible with your vehicle? It makes no sense, for example, having a wheel (lug) wrench that does not fit into the bolts on the wheels of your vehicle.

Turn the pages to discover more about the outside of your vehicle and what to put in your trunk.

Body of Your Vehicle

Washing

- Wash your vehicle when its body is cool from top to bottom and out of direct sunlight. Use lukewarm to cold water and add car-washing solution, not dish detergent.

- When washing your vehicle, spray wash underneath it, including the wheel wells, to remove gravel, mud, salt, sand, and other grime.

- Hubcaps and wheels often require special cleaning compounds, depending on what they are made of (for example, aluminum or chrome).

- Use a wet cloth, rather than a dry one, to remove bird droppings, dirt, and tree sap from your vehicle's body.

- Lower the power antenna and turn the side-view mirrors in when taking your vehicle through power washes. This prevents damage from the high-powered brushes.

- During winter, wash your vehicle, including the underside and wheel wheels, at least once a week to remove ice, slush, snow, and salt build-up.

- Door latches and locks can freeze after going through a car wash, especially in winter. To prevent this, lightly lubricate the door and trunk locks and gas cap so that water cannot penetrate the holes.

WOO WEE, I LIKE IT !!
I LIKE IT !!

Waxing

- Waxing helps keep your vehicle cleaner for a longer period of time than if no wax is applied.

- Wax your vehicle when its body is cool and away from direct sunlight as the sun can cause spotting.

- Waxing the weather-stripping around a sunroof often decreases how effective the stripping can provide a tight seal.

- The most effective wax has ingredients that block out ultraviolet rays.

THIS IS ONE TIME I REALLY KNOW SHE LOVES ME

Rust

- Rust spots and dents interfere with the overall look of your vehicle, which is particularly important for resale purposes.

- Body rust usually starts around the trim at the front and rear windows or where moisture accumulates.

- Small paint chips on your vehicle can turn into rust spots. Purchase a can of touch-up paint to cover the nicks and scrapes.

- To combat rust, automobile manufacturers are making body parts, such as doors, hoods, and trunks, out of polymers (synthetics or plastics), which are not prone to rust. Automakers are also making vehicle components more rounded, so that moisture has no place to accumulate.

- There is a difference between rust proofing and undercoating. Rust proofing is a coating applied to the insides of body panels, such as doors, fenders, and the hood. The compounds and systems used to rust proof provide varying degrees of effectiveness. However, there is no such thing as a fully rust proof vehicle. Undercoating is sprayed to the underside of your vehicle to protect it against rust. Undercoating also reduces road noise.

Doors

- Strict side-impact protection standards have been introduced that require automobile manufacturers to install protective beams inside the door panels. These beams, also referred to as "crash-zones," help reduce the impact of a side collision.

- If your vehicle is equipped with side air bags, the sensors activating them are located along the side-impact beams.

- Remote control, keyless entry systems are available on some vehicles. This means you don't require a key to unlock your vehicle's doors, which is handy if your arms are full of groceries.

- To prevent door locks from freezing in winter, especially after going through a car wash, lubricate the locks so that water cannot penetrate the small holes. Or, lightly coat the door key with oil and insert it in the lock a few times to lubricate it on the inside.

- Heat the tip of a small screwdriver and put it in the lock, or use a squirt of gas-line antifreeze to melt a frozen door lock.

Gas Cap

- If the gas cap is cracked or bulging, replace it with a manufacturer-approved cap.

- Never drive your vehicle without a gas cap.

- Before driving up to a gas pump, know which side of your vehicle the gas cap is on.

- Never overfill the fuel tank, but do keep it as full as possible to avoid running out of gas and prevent water droplets from collecting inside the tank.

- Smoking while pumping gas is not only a safety hazard, it is probably illegal.

- Never siphon fuel from the gas cap; a surge of fuel can engulf your lungs.

- Keep an old pair of gloves in the trunk of your vehicle. On cold days, wear the gloves when filling the tank at a self-service gas station.

- In winter, add approximately 150 ml ($^2/_3$ c.) of gas-line antifreeze once a week to prevent the gas tank and fuel line from freezing.

- During spring, summer, and fall, add 150 ml ($^2/_3$ c.) of gas-line antifreeze once a month to prevent moisture from accumulating inside the fuel tank.

AM I HALF EMPTY, OR HALF FULL ?
I GUESS THAT DEPENDS ON MY MOOD

- Sometimes changing the brand of gas affects engine performance. For example, engine idling may improve.

- To remove the gas cap, slowly turn it counterclockwise. To reinsert the gas cap, slowly turn it clockwise until you hear a click. Overtightening the cap adds pressure, which makes it difficult to remove.

- At full-service gas stations, make sure the attendant correctly reinserts the gas cap.

- Gas can cause paint damage so try not to spill fuel onto the body of your vehicle.

- Alternatives for fuel include propane, natural gas, methanol, electricity, and hydrogen. Of these alternatives, hydrogen has the greatest potential to be the least expensive way to operate a vehicle.

Hood

- Know how to open the hood on your vehicle. The hood release latch is either at the front grille or inside your vehicle where it is usually to the left of the driver's seat.

- Once the latch is released, lift, press, or pull the lever at the front grille to raise the hood up. A rod is sometimes needed to keep the hood open. This long metal rod sits along the front grille and hooks into a hole at the top of the underside of the hood. If there is no rod, the hood should stay open by itself.

- Hood locks prevent thieves from tampering with the engine or disabling the alarm system.

Lights

What Lights Up Your Vehicle

Back-up Lights

- ➤ Back-up lights are the white lights at the back of your vehicle.

- ➤ A white light should be visible when the transmission is in "R."

- ➤ Sometimes a back-up light switch is located on the transmission shift linkage.

Brake Lights

- ➤ Brake lights are the red lights at the back of your vehicle.

- ➤ A red light goes on when the brake pedal is depressed. "Riding the brakes" confuses drivers behind you as the light is activated even though you do not intend to brake.

Daytime Running Lights (DRL)

- ➤ Most daytime running lights (DRL) activate the front lights when your vehicle is turned on.

- ➤ Most vehicles with DRL do not light up the back of your vehicle, nor do they light up the dashboard.

- ➤ Daytime running lights offer extra illumination only during daylight hours and weather permitting, such as when visibility is clear. They should never be used in place of headlights.

➤ Daytime running lights are not as bright as low beams. Low beams offer improved visibility for you and other motorists so it is safer to use low beams during the day, rather than relying on DRL, especially when visibility is poor.

Fog Lights

➤ Usually located below the bumper, fog lights are amber, orange, or white. Amber is an easy colour on the eyes, orange offers no benefits, and white fog lamps emit maximum light transmission.

➤ Fog lights offer improved visibility in weather conditions, such as fog, rain, or snow, as the light shines closer to the pavement and farther out to the sides.

➤ When driving in fog, use fog lights or low beams and activate the hazard flasher. This increases your vehicle's visibility to other drivers. Unless absolutely necessary, do not stop your vehicle. If you must pull over, park well off the roadway. Put the parking lights on. Should you decide to leave your vehicle, place a note on the dashboard (see *AutoTalk Assistant*).

Hazard Flasher

➤ The hazard flasher can be activated while you are driving and your vehicle is having difficulties, when there is heavy fog, or when you are driving considerably slower than the posted speed limit.

➤ Use the hazard flasher only when your vehicle is disabled on or off the road, where a vehicle would not normally stop.

➤ A hazard flasher is a temporary warning device only. A flasher left on for any length of time will drain your vehicle's battery.

Headlights

➤ Activate the low beams from one hour before dusk to one hour after dawn or if visibility deteriorates during daylight hours.

➤ Effective headlights are white. Blue headlights don't offer the necessary visibility and are probably illegal.

➤ Halogen headlights offer increased lighting power, which is advantageous, for example, in rural areas where there are no street lights.

➤ High-intensity headlights are designed to provide increased light without the glare.

➤ Operating your vehicle with one headlight burned out is a safety hazard as visibility is greatly reduced for yourself and other motorists.

➤ Use low beams in rain, snow, or if there is smoke in the air. Fog lights are used in fog.

➤ Aim headlights so that the light shines on the road directly in front of your vehicle, rather than to either side. Know the legal minimum distances for headlights to project light.

➤ Align headlights when your vehicle is on level ground, when it is not loaded down with extra weight, when all the tires have the appropriate air pressure, and when the fuel tank is at least one-half full.

➤ If you want the headlights to be aimed as accurately as possible, bounce your vehicle a couple of times before aligning the lights.

➤ To see if the headlights are properly positioned, shine them on your garage door or at a wall.

➤ When replacing a headlight, use the same wattage as the burned-out headlight. Installing a higher wattage distorts vision, for you and other motorists.

➤ Check the positioning of headlights when changing from snow tires to summer or all season radial tires.

Parking Lights

➤ Parking lights are used when parking in areas that have limited light.

➤ Never drive using the parking lights, especially in fog, as they do not project sufficient light.

Signal Lights

➤ The signal bulbs for the two front signal lights are located under the hood, on each side of your vehicle.

➤ The signal bulbs for the two rear signal lights are usually located inside the trunk.

Lights On!

- To ensure maximum visibility for you and other motorists, clean all the exterior lights of dirt, oil, and other grime using a wet cloth.

- Cracks in the front and back lights reduce your vehicle's visibility for other drivers.

- Turn off all exterior lights around your vehicle before replacing any bulbs.

- To change a bulb, push the old bulb in and then turn it counterclockwise. Insert the new bulb by pushing it in the socket and then turning it clockwise.

- Before changing a burned-out bulb, clean the bulb base of dirt particles.

- Touching the bulb with your fingers coats it with oil, which reduces its effectiveness. Clean the bulb with alcohol if your fingers touched it.

- Replace bulbs with the same type and rating indicated on the burned-out bulb.

Racks – Hitch, Roof, and Trunk

- Racks do not increase your vehicle's ability to hold weight. They simply offer a place to store the maximum payload capacity for your car or multi-purpose vehicle.

- A *hitch* rack is a heavy-duty rack that is attached to a trailer hitch. A *roof* rack is a multi-purpose rack attached to the top of your vehicle, and a *trunk* rack sits on your vehicle's bumper.

- When purchasing a hitch, roof, or trunk rack, consider the following: what the rack will be used for, whether the rack will be switched from one vehicle to another or remain a permanent fixture on your vehicle, if locks will be needed to secure what the rack is holding, whether you want the items on the rack hidden from view, and how wind gusts and other weather conditions will affect the items on the rack and your ability to handle your vehicle.

- The added weight of what's on the hitch, roof, or trunk rack can cause the transmission to overheat, especially if driving uphill for long distances.

- Factory racks may not be strong enough to withstand the weight of certain items. Installing an attachment to the factory rack usually enables it to carry the extra weight.

- Before installing a roof rack, clear dirt, ice, and snow from the roof.

- The roof rack should be secured to the top of your vehicle. Periodically check the rack to ensure that the attachment points are tight.

- Tightly secure everything onto the roof rack. Parts of a rack and other items have been known to blow off a vehicle, causing damage to other automobiles and, in some cases, injury to motorists.

- A loaded roof rack affects how your vehicle moves. Be careful when making turns and going around curves.

Side-View Mirrors

- Adjust the driver and passenger side-view mirrors only after you are safely positioned in the driver's seat.

- Focus each mirror so that you can see the driver's door and the passenger's door.

- Driver and passenger side-view mirrors have blind spots. When changing lanes, always shoulder check, in addition to looking in the mirrors. Remember to signal as well.

- Power mirrors are difficult to repair and replace as most of the cable connections are complex.

- If you do need to replace a side-view mirror, use oversized screws to firmly attach the mirror to the body frame - the screw holes on the frame become enlarged from the old mirror.

- Never lubricate the side-view mirror cables with oil. Dirt and dust will collect on the cables. Use silicone spray instead.

- A side minder is a reflective device attached to the side-view mirror. When an oncoming vehicle approaches your vehicle, the side minder flashes, indicating the vehicle behind you is within 2.7 m (9 ft.). In other words, the vehicle is in your blind spot. This device is a recent innovation and is not yet widely available.

Tires

Sidewall Markings on Tires

The following cites an example of the letters, numbers, and markings that appear on the sidewall of a tire. You can easily adapt this information to the tires on your vehicle.

32 PSI (Pounds per Square Inch) or 220 kPa (Kilopascals) Max. Pressure

➤ The PSI indicates maximum amount of air pressure, which must not be exceeded when the tire is cold.

➤ This number probably differs from what your vehicle owner's manual indicates for maximum tire pressure. Use the PSI specified by the vehicle manufacturer to inflate the tires on your vehicle.

Max. load 630 kg (1400 lb.)

➤ The total kilograms (pounds) tell you how much weight the tires can support.

➤ This number is especially important when taking a trip with added passengers and luggage.

WHOOPS!! A LITTLE TOO MUCH

All seasons

➤ These tires are built to handle most weather conditions.

➤ Sometimes symbols indicating the four seasons are moulded onto the tire sidewall.

P205/70 SR 14

➤ *P* = Passenger vehicle. LT means light trucks.

➤ *205* = Tire width from sidewall to sidewall.

➤ *70* = Percentage of tire height vs. tire width.

➤ *S* = Speed rating. Letters start at "S" and go to "T". "S" indicates the tire can reach a maximum speed of 180 km/h (112 mph).

➤ *R* = Radial.

➤ *14* = Rim diameter (in inches).

DOT (Tire Identification Number)

➤ These letters and numbers are useful if the tire has been recalled.

➤ The last three digits indicate the week and year the tire was made. Purchase only new tires that have been built within the past year.

AA

➤ These letters and numbers work in conjunction with the Uniform Tire Quality Grading (UTQG) system.

➤ Tire manufacturers tend to assign ratings to their tires only. Comparing the UTQG between tire brands is not as useful as measuring traction and temperature within a manufacturer's product line of tires.

➤ A (first letter) = Traction (ability for the tire to stop on wet pavement, not how the tire performs on dry roads). "A" is the highest rating and "C" the lowest.

➤ A (second letter) = Temperature (tire's ability to handle heat). "A" is the highest rating and "C" the lowest.

Tread Wear Index

➤ The numbers range from 100 to 500. The higher the number, the longer the tire should last.

Tire Pressure

- For full riding comfort and safety, and for fewer tire repair bills, inflate all tires to the weight stated in your vehicle's specifications, rather than what is indicated on the sidewall of the tire.

- Your vehicle's specification for tire pressure is found in the vehicle owner's manual, inside the driver's door, or on a sticker inside the glove compartment.

- Some vehicle specifications for tire pressure indicate the letter "F" (front tires) and "R" (rear tires).

- The most common tire pressure is between 28 and 32 PSI (192 and 220 kPa).

- Invest in a good quality tire pressure gauge. Make sure it reads kilopascals as well as pounds and that it reads up to 60 lb. (410 kPa).

- Check air pressure in the tires when they are cold.

- Tire pressure decreases 0.5 kg (1 lb.) for every 5 degrees Celsius (or 10 degrees Fahrenheit) the temperature drops. This is especially important to remember during winter, so always maintain adequate air pressure in all tires, including the spare.

- A tire can be over- or underinflated, which can result in a tire blowout or vehicle handling and braking difficulties. An overinflated tire shows excessive tread wear in its middle whereas an underinflated tire exhibits heavy wear on each of its sides.

- Air seeping from the tire inflation valve stem can cause a tire leak. This often happens when the temperature is cold as the stem and cap freeze and then crack.

- Consider replacing the short valve stem on the tire with a longer one so that it's easier to use the tire pressure gauge.

Tire Rotation

- By rotating the tires on your vehicle, you maintain an even wear on all tires, which makes for a smoother running vehicle. Rotating tires does not prolong the life of tires.

- A rule of thumb is to rotate your tires every 8,000 to 12,000 km (5,000 to 7,000 mi.), depending on where you drive. City driving means lots of road bumps, potholes, and abrupt turns, while long stretches of highway results in more even wear on the tires.

- How vehicles are built and tires constructed determine how tires are rotated. For example, whether your vehicle is front wheel or rear wheel drive and the type of tires on your vehicle depends on tire rotation procedures.

- Rotating one set of tires in an "X" (crisscross) pattern and then exchanging the other set with their direct opposites at the front or rear is the most common rotation method.

Tire Tread

- You can feel for bumps or uneven wear on a tire by rubbing your hand across it.

- Tires that have glass, nails, stones, and other objects lodged in them can cause a slow air leak or a blowout while driving. Cracked or bulging tires or ones with exposed chords are also indications a flat is forthcoming.

- Many tires have tread wear indicators (or "wear bars") moulded across two or more tread grooves. When the treads wear down to 1.6 mm (.06 in.), the tire needs to be replaced.

- A simple way to check a tire's tread is to put a penny into the tread groove. If the top of the Queen's (Lincoln's) head is visible, replace the tire.

Tire Wheels (Rims) and Hubcaps

- Tire wheels (rims) should not be bent, cracked, or rusted.

- Clean inside the wheels (rims) before installing replacement tires.

- Note the size of the rim diameter. This designation must match the tire diameter. For example, a 35.6 cm (14 in.) tire diameter must be mounted on a 35.6 cm (14 in.) rim and not on a 36.8 cm (14 $^1/_2$ in.) rim.

- Loose or missing lugs (nuts) from the wheels can cause the tire to wobble or fall off while your vehicle is moving, even at slow speeds.

- Never use oil or grease on the wheel lugs (nuts) and bolts (threads). Lubrication causes the lugs to loosen while your vehicle is being driven.

- Hubcaps prevent dust and dirt from entering the brakes.

- Periodically check that the hubcaps are tightly secured to the wheels (rims).

Types of Tires

- Categories of tires include bias ply tires, bias belted tires, and radial tires. Tires are also grouped into all-season, performance, all-season performance, and snow tires.

- Bias ply tires reflect the way tires were originally constructed. They are no longer common on vehicles.

- Bias belted tires add stability in vehicle movement.

- Radial tires minimize tire wear and improve vehicle handling, especially at corners.

- Radial tires are sensitive to air pressure. They also tend to look soft and appear underinflated.

- All-season radials handle all types of road conditions, including ice- and snow-covered roads. They are the most common tires on new vehicles.

- Radial tires labeled premium are made with more cuts in the rubber. They also have precipitated silica built into the rubber compound, which improves traction on ice, slush, and snow.

- Performance tires are used primarily on sports vehicles and luxury sedans.

- All-season performance tires combine the features of all-season radial tires and the traction and stability associated with performance tires.

- Snow tires have specially formulated rubber that improves traction on ice- and snow-covered surfaces. However, they tend to be noisy, increase fuel consumption, and do not last long on dry roads. You should avoid using snow tires during the spring, summer, and fall.

- As a new standard set by tire manufacturers, snow tires now have a letter "M" (mud) or "S" (snow) stamped to their sidewalls, and are accompanied with a six-sided snowflake inside a three-peaked mountain design.

- Install snow tires on all the wheels if your vehicle is front wheel drive or has antilock brakes and you want to a maintain more even traction on each wheel. If you have a rear wheel drive vehicle, use snow tires on the rear wheels only. Put on four snow tires if you have a four-wheel drive vehicle.

- To assist tires in doing their job, automobile manufacturers are installing electronic traction control (ETC) on some vehicles. Be aware of the limitations of this system as well as its strengths, which includes reducing power when the tires start spinning.

Wheel Balancing and Wheel Alignment

- Having the wheels balanced compensates for irregularities in tire construction. A small lead weight affixed to the wheel (rim) stabilizes the tire.

- There are two ways to balance a tire on its wheel (rim): static (the tire is off your vehicle) and dynamic (the tire is still on your vehicle). Of the two methods, request dynamic balancing as it also compensates for brakes and suspension parts on your vehicle.

- Wheel balancing should be included when purchasing and installing new tires. A wheel alignment is not always necessary, depending on how much tread wear is on the old tires. If the old tires are uniformly worn down, a wheel alignment is not required.

- A wheel alignment keeps the wheels moving in the same direction.

- All tires must be properly inflated before a wheel alignment is done.

- If the wheels are not aligned, the tires become uneven very quickly.

- Under normal driving conditions, the front tires should be positioned slightly at an angle to the frame. Called "toe-in," these tires appear pigeon-toed. Or, the front tires should look like a Charlie Chaplain stand (called "toe-out"). If either position is exaggerated, the wheels are out of alignment.

- Driving over potholes and hitting curbs when turning and parking can put the front wheels out of alignment.

- Some vehicles, such as those with independent rear suspension, require that the rear wheels be aligned, in addition to the front wheels.

More to Say about Tires

- Statistics indicate that one of the three most common on road vehicle breakdowns involves tires. This usually means a flat tire, which was caused by low tire inflation, poor tire tread, or an improper wheel alignment.

- The overall weight of your vehicle affects tire wear. Never load your vehicle above its maximum allowed weight, taking into consideration passengers and other cargo as part of the equation.

- Using your vehicle's largest recommended tire size increases gas mileage, improves steering abilities, and adds to riding comfort.

- Immediately inspect all tires on your vehicle after driving through a skid or heavily braking. Unusual vehicle movement may result in a flat spot appearing on the tire.

- Excessive speed and pressure can cause a tire to explode. This is especially important to remember when trying to get your vehicle out of a stuck situation since the tires are constantly spinning.

- When selecting tires, consider where and how much your vehicle will be driven. Through lots of ice and snow? On long highway trips?

- New tires on your vehicle must be broken in. Drive at slower speeds for the first 100 km (60 mi.).

- Ideally, purchase tires in pairs and make sure they have the same sidewall markings.

- If you are purchasing only two new tires, mount them at the front since these wheels usually provide most of the braking ability.

- Tire sealers are for small tire leaks. Use sealers only in an emergency and drive to the nearest service centre to have the tire repaired since sealers can be difficult to remove. Other products are applied to the inside of a tire that permanently seal tire punctures as they occur.

- A smart tire has been designed that uses microscopic temperature and pressure sensors to indicate when the tire is going flat or when it should be replaced.

- Old tires are enjoying the recycling process. Rubber mattresses for cattle (yes, cows) and rubber crumb for playgrounds and golf courses are examples where scrap tires are shredded into tiny chips and then further processed into rubber crumb.

- Store tires on their rims and at the maximum PSI indicated on their sidewall. Lay the tires on the floor of your garage; never stand them up on their sides and keep them away from fridges and freezers.

Trunk

For added safety while on the road, the trunk of your vehicle should contain a number of tools and other supplies. Keep these items in your trunk all year round. They don't take up that much room; the trick is to keep them organized in covered plastic or rubber containers.

Emergency Package

- Small *backpack* (to carry supplies if you decide to leave your vehicle or you must evacuate the area)
- *Cloth bag* (in case someone is locked inside the trunk) containing a pair of pliers, screwdriver, extra trunk remote opener (periodically test its batteries) if your vehicle is equipped with one, and a small working flashlight
- *Baking soda* (to smother a small fire, such as a cigarette butt smoldering in the interior)
- *Batteries* for the flashlight and transistor radio (by wrapping the batteries individually, they last longer)
- Wool *blanket* or sleeping bag
- *Candles* and an empty tin for holding a lit candle
- Loose *change* to make a phone call if you don't have a cellular phone or it has a low battery
- *Children's items* (if you frequently travel with an infant/child), such as activity books, canned milk, diapers, and heavier clothes (boots, hat, mitts, scarf, socks, and a sweater)
- Piece of white or brightly coloured *cloth* to tie to the radio antenna or door handle on the side nearest traffic
- Personal *clothing* (lined boots, hat, mittens, scarf, wool socks, and a heavy sweater)
- Small *flashlight* (with batteries removed)
- Non-perishable *food* items, such as candies, crackers, gum (a wad of gum can also be used to temporarily seal holes in pipes, etc.), honey, jam, and sugar (replace these food items once a year)
- Extra set of vehicle *door keys* (make sure you always have an extra trunk key, or remote control opener, on you)

*HA!!... AND THEY SAID I WAS BEING
OVERLY PREPARED! WHO'S LAUGHING NOW!*

- *Kitty litter*, newspapers, carpet remnants, a bag of salt, or a traction mat (to provide traction under the tires); sand is not recommended as its high moisture content can freeze into a lump in cold temperatures
- Wooden *matches* (dip the ends in fingernail polish and wrap in plastic to keep them from getting damp), waterproof matches, or a cigarette lighter
- Outdoor *survival kit* (in a fanny pack include a compass, keychain flashlight, pocket knife, compact plastic raincoat (or an orange garbage bag), a bag of high energy trail mix, a small bottle of drinking water, and a whistle)
- Transistor *radio* (with batteries removed)
- *Reading material* and deck of cards to pass the time
- *Reflective tape* can be taped over a burned-out head or tail light or across the hood, roof, or trunk to make your vehicle more visible
- *Reflectors* (safer than flares)
- *Shovel* and axe
- *Sign* indicating "Help" or "Police" (see *AutoTalk Assistant*)
- Bottle of *soda water* to clean spills on the interior seats
- *Drinking water* (need 1 L [1 qt.] per adult per day)

First Aid Kit

- *Bandages* and gauze of various sizes
- Reflective rescue *blanket*
- *Cold packs*
- List of *emergency* names and phone numbers (see *AutoTalk Assistant*)
- *Non-prescription medication* (Aspirin, Tylenol, decongestant tablets, antiseptic cream)
- *Prescription medication* (in original containers)
- First aid *procedures booklet*
- *Rubbing alcohol*
- *Safety pins* (various sizes)
- *Scissors*
- *Syringes* and other personal medical supplies
- *Tweezers*

Tools and Supplies

- Premixed *antifreeze* (50% antifreeze with 50% water or a 60/40 mixture)
- *Automatic transmission fluid* (if your vehicle is an automatic)
- *Booster (battery) cables* (5 m [16 ft], 16 gauge with sturdy clamps)
- Various sizes of signal and other light *bulbs*
- *Brake fluid* (small unopened can)
- Various sizes of *clamps* (gear type clamps are the easiest to use)
- *Coat hanger* or soft wire to tie down a loose muffler or exhaust pipe
- Lock *de-icer*
- Litre (quart) of *engine oil* (same weight and grade as what's in the engine)
- Used *fan belt*
- *Funnel*
- Various *fuses* (correct size and rating for your vehicle)
- Empty *gas container* (a full container can result in an explosion)
- Gas-line *antifreeze*

- Rubber or plastic and wool *gloves*
- *Hammer*
- Bumper, side lift, or scissors *jack* with a four-sided wheel (lug) wrench, a jack stand, a piece of board to place underneath the jack stand, and a piece of long pipe to fit into the lug wrench
- Old kitchen *knife*
- *Pliers* (one pair needle-nose pliers to grasp small parts, one pair slip-joint pliers for larger objects, and one pair Vise-Grips (a locking jaw plier) for hard to grasp items
- *Power steering fluid* (small unopened can)
- Clean *rags* or paper towels
- *Rope* or towing chain
- *Screws* and bolts (various sizes, secured in a small plastic bag)
- Oversized, bright colored old *shirt* for when you must work on your vehicle unexpectedly
- *Screwdrivers* (one flathead and one Phillips)
- *Snow brush* with an attached ice scraper
- Duct *tape* to label parts
- *Tin foil* to temporarily place over a fuel line
- *Tire pressure gauge*
- *Tire inflation valves* (long and short stems)
- *Water*
- *WD-40*
- *Windshield washer fluid*
- *Wrenches* (one ratchet wrench [a closed wrench where the end rotates] and one Crescent wrench [it has an adjustable end])

Spare Tire

- Routinely test the air pressure in the spare tire.

- Rust problems in the trunk usually start underneath the spare tire.

- It is necessary to have only one good quality spare tire (with adequate air pressure) in the trunk, even if it is a compact spare. An extra tire in the trunk adds unnecessary weight to your vehicle, increasing fuel consumption.

- Compact spares are temporary and should be used in an emergency only. They are marked on the sidewall "temporary with 60 PSI" (or another poundage). They are also smaller than a regular tire.

- Do not drive for more than 100 km (60 mi.) with a compact spare on one of your vehicle's wheels.

- Never go faster than 80 km/h (50 mph), or what speed is indicated on the sidewall of the compact spare.

- A compact spare affects steering and braking abilities.

- Taking your vehicle through an automatic car wash with the compact spare can damage the wheel and other vehicle parts.

- Using a tire chain on a compact spare can damage the chain, the tire, and other vehicle parts.

Trunk Release Device

- A trunk release device offers protection for children who inadvertently lock themselves inside the trunk or someone who is put in the trunk against her or his will.

- An automotive dealership or an auto-alarm dealer can install a trunk release device. Or, you can install one yourself.

- One of the major automobile manufacturers has designed a retrofitted, inside-the-trunk release kit (an industry first). Installed by a dealership, the kit includes a bright yellow handle that attaches to the inside of the trunk. This kit can be installed on specific makes of passenger vehicles built after 1990.

- Make sure your children know this device exists and how to use it. Ensure they know how to get out of the trunk if no device exits by using the contents in the cloth bag described in the preceding page.

Vehicle Registration and Insurance

- As a safety precaution, hide your vehicle registration and insurance in a discreet location in the trunk, rather than in the glove compartment.

Windows and Windshield Wipers

Windows

- Periodically wash the windows using a combination of vinegar and warm water. This removes grease and wax build-up. In cold temperatures, add 25 ml (2 tbsp.) of rubbing alcohol to the water to prevent ice formation on the windshield.

- Periodically applying water repellent to the windows helps rain and snow roll off the windshield.

- Clear leaves, ice, snow, and other obstructions from the hood and inlet grates at the front of the windshield. Otherwise, the windows will fog up.

- Gas-line antifreeze can be used to defrost an ice-covered windshield.

- Never use hot water to de-ice windows; the windows may crack.

- Wipe water from the top of the sunroof before opening it.

- Periodically open the sunroof year-round so that it doesn't stick.

- Tinted windows keep the interior cool, prevent fading on the seats and dashboard, and offer privacy. Some provincial (state) governments mandate that only the rear side and back windows can be tinted.

Windshield Wipers

- A small motor, a fuse, and one or two switches operate the windshield wipers. Each of these parts can become defective.

- Brittle, cracked, or discoloured wiper blades are not effective in clearing and cleaning your vehicle's windows. Worn-out wiper blades can also scratch the windows.

- Streaking on the windows when the wiper blades are used is often the result of tar, tree sap, or other grime caked onto the rubber. Wash the rubbers with washer fluid and use a soft cloth to wipe dry.

- Using the wiper blades when the windshield is dry may scratch the window.

- Turn the wiper blades switch off before turning the ignition off. Make sure the blades are in the down position.

- Before activating the wiper blades switch, clear ice or snow from the wiper blades and make sure the rubbers are not frozen to the windows.

- The weight of heavy snow can cause activated wiper blades to break.

- To remove slush and snow from the blades, lift them from the window and use your hand to wipe them off. Or, lift the blades and let them drop back onto the window. By doing this, you get rid of ice build-up, which makes the wiper blades easier to use the next time you operate your vehicle.

- Rubber warps in warm temperatures and cracks in the cold. Change all wiper blades, including the rear blade, every six months (to coincide with spring and fall).

- "Winterized" wiper blades are covered with a protective rubber coating. They are also constructed in such a way that the rubber itself stays flat on the windshield. These features prevent ice and snow from sticking to the blades.

HA!!! NEW WIPERS! BRING ON THE RAIN!

- Some wiper blades are built with Teflon coating on the rubber. This extends the life of the rubber blade and reduces streaking. These blades also fit nicely around contoured windshields.

- The metal part on the wiper blades may become damaged from car wash equipment and ice scrapers.

- Debris sitting in the area under the hood (around the cowl) can affect movement of the wiper blades.

- The nozzles (spray tips) for the windshield wipers should always be clear of obstructions and appropriately positioned. To adjust the nozzles, use your fingers or a pair of pliers and cautiously twist them.

- Sometimes a nozzle becomes clogged. Clean it with a needle or straight pin or by blowing into the nozzle itself. If the nozzle is too clogged, it may require replacing.

- Some vehicles are equipped with heated windshield nozzles.

Section 3
Under the Hood

This section uncovers engine parts under the hood. Where each part is located and what it does all blend together to make your vehicle run smoothly. Keeping the engine well maintained ensures it is safe and reliable while your vehicle is being driven.

For specific information on what's under the hood of your car or multi-purpose vehicle (minivan, light truck, or sport-utility vehicle), consult the owner's manual.

SECTION THREE CONTENTS

...cont'd

...cont'd

...cont'd

...cont'd

Introduction

It's important to know what sits where under the hood of *your* vehicle, rather than examining someone else's engine or looking at generic pictures of engine parts. Take what you read in this section and apply it to the vehicle you drive. Once this visual connection is made, become more familiar with what the part does and gather some handy maintenance and other engine tid-bits by reviewing the following pages.

Here are some suggestions for when you are inspecting what's under the hood of your vehicle.

- Tie your hair back and remove jewellery, such as watches and rings, before opening the hood. Once the engine is exposed, put on a pair of plastic or rubber gloves.
- Always work in an area that has lots of fresh air.
- The buddy system works well any time you look at the engine of a vehicle.
- Keep a fire extinguisher handy.
- Check fluid levels when your vehicle is on level ground.
- Fluids, such as antifreeze are poisonous in taste and smell. Keep them away from children, pets, and other animals and wash your hands thoroughly after looking under the hood.
- Add fluids that are recommended by the manufacturer or in your vehicle owner's manual.
- Check bolts, cables, and clamps to be sure they are snug. Do not overtighten or leave them too loose.

Turn the pages to discover more about what's under the hood and how these parts work together to keep the engine running smoothly.

Air Cleaner and Air Filter

Where They Are

The air *cleaner* is a black metal or plastic container often located beside the fuel-injection system. On vehicles with carburetors, the air cleaner sits on top of the carburetor. The air *filter* is round or square pleated sheets of paper that fits inside the air cleaner.

What They Do

The air cleaner and air filter help keep dust and other air impurities from entering and damaging the engine.

Filtering the Air

- Air filters come in various colours, shapes, and sizes of pleated paper folds.

- Check the air filter by holding it up to the light. If you can see light through the filter, it is still clean enough to continue using. Some filters are deceiving, though, and show no light coming through the clean paper folds and they let light shine through a dirty filter.

- Never clean the air filter with water since this damages the pleated sheets. Rather, lightly tap the filter against a flat surface to remove some of the dirt particles.

- Wipe dirt and dust from the air cleaner before installing a new filter.

- Insert the new air filter the same way you removed the old filter.

- Some owner's manuals recommend that a professional mechanic remove an old air filter and install a new one so that it is properly positioned.

Air Conditioning Unit

Where It Is

Extending from close to the radiator, the air conditioning unit works its way around the engine block to end at the evaporator, which is usually located inside your vehicle.

What It Does

All the parts of the air conditioning unit absorb and release heat to cool the air inside your vehicle.

Parts of the Air Conditioner

• The air conditioning unit includes the blower motor, condenser (a radiator-like part), compressor (a belt-driven pump), evaporator (a row of coils), expansion valve (regulates the flow of refrigerant), hoses and clamps, the receiver/dryer (a filter that removes moisture from the refrigerant), and the refrigerant (the fluid).

• Never tamper with air conditioning hoses and clamps as the fluid (refrigerant) inside the hoses may explode. Have a professional mechanic perform any work on the air conditioner.

• There are different clamps on air conditioning hoses than on other hoses, such as radiator hoses.

• Newer vehicles are equipped with environmentally friendly refrigerant (non-freon). This CFC free refrigerant has the label R-134a, rather than the old R-12 refrigerant.

• Vehicles having old refrigerant can be converted or recharged with a non-combustible refrigerant, such as FR-12. Never use butane or propane in the air conditioning unit. You don't want pressurized explosive gases running through the system and ending up inside your vehicle.

• An air conditioning unit can be installed in your vehicle, as long as there is enough space under the hood.

Alternator

Where It Is

The round and silver coloured alternator is usually located at the front of the engine, near the bottom. It has a belt attached to it that is also affixed to the crankshaft (below the engine block).

What It Does

The alternator keeps the battery charged, while also working with other electrical components, such as the starter, to ignite the engine and keep it running.

As Part of the Charging System

- The alternator can become defective if the battery is not fully charging.

- Corroded battery cables often affect the alternator's ability to maintain a charge.

- A belt connects the alternator to the crankshaft. This belt can loosen or slip, causing the alternator to not work properly.

- The alternator belt may also be attached to the water pump.

- A voltage regulator manages the amount of electricity the alternator charges to the battery. Most regulators are installed at the alternator, although some are incorporated into the alternator itself.

- A voltage regulator can become defective. If the regulator must be replaced, install a new alternator as well, even if it is not defective.

Automatic Transmission Fluid and Dipstick

Where They Are

The automatic transmission dipstick is usually located behind or in front of the engine. The dipstick extends into an automatic transmission pan, which houses the fluid.

What They Do

Transmission fluid lubricates the automatic gears. The dipstick reads the amount and quality of fluid inside the automatic transmission pan.

Reading the Dipstick

- Automatic transmission fluid should always be reddish in colour.

- Do not confuse the transmission dipstick with the oil dipstick, which is usually higher than the transmission dipstick. The dipstick tops are often different colours. Some dipsticks also have "trans fluid" printed on them.

- The hole this dipstick extends into is larger than the hole for the oil dipstick. Why? Transmission fluid is poured into this hole using a funnel, whereas engine oil is added through a large fill hole sitting at the top of the engine.

- With your vehicle on level ground, check the transmission fluid when the engine is hot and idling. The gear should be set to either "N" or "P" (depending on the make of vehicle), and the parking brake engaged. On some vehicles, the engine must be turned off to get a reliable reading of the transmission fluid level.

- For an accurate reading of the transmission fluid level, pull the dipstick, wipe it clean, reinsert it, pull it out again, then read the level. The fluid should be at the full mark, not below and never above. You can also touch the liquid on the dipstick. It should feel warm, not hot.

- The dipstick reads the amount of transmission fluid. Look at the two grooves on the dipstick. Some sticks also have the letters "E" (empty) and "F" (full) imprinted on them, or they are marked with temperatures. The amount of fluid between the two marks equals 0.5 L. (½ qt.).

- Reinsert the dipstick making sure no dirt or water enter through the dipstick opening.

- Transmission fluid on hot engine parts can result in a fire. To prevent spills, use a special funnel having a long tube when adding transmission fluid.

- Use only automatic transmission fluid recommended by the vehicle manufacturer.

- Old automatic transmission fluid can result in poor shifting of gears or total transmission failure

THE OIL OR TRANNY...
WHICH STICK IS WHICH?

Battery

Where It Is

The battery most often sits to one side at the front of the engine. It has two cables, one positive (+) and one negative (–), extending from its posts. One cable goes to the starter and starter solenoid and the other, usually the negative cable, goes to the engine.

What It Does

The battery passes on electrical current necessary to operate the ignition system and other electrical accessories.

As Part of the Electrical System

- The positive terminal is usually the larger post on a battery.

- Always *disconnect* the negative terminal first, to avoid sparking, and *connect* the positive terminal first.

- Any time the battery cables have been disconnected and then connected again, memory features, such as radio programming and the alarm code, must be re-entered. Make sure you know the manufacturer's code for the alarm system prior to disconnecting the battery cables.

- The battery should sit on a flat surface under the hood and be secured with holding clamps. Never overtighten the clamps as this can crack the battery case. The battery should not slide or bounce, especially when your vehicle is moving.

- The solution in the battery is a combination of sulphuric acid and water (called electrolyte). It is highly combustible and poisonous. Never smoke when around a battery nor get any electrolyte on your hands and face.

- There must always be one vent cap for every battery cell. Tightly secure each vent cap onto the battery.

- Some batteries may require adding distilled water (tap water has too many minerals) by way of the vent caps. Wipe the top of the battery after adding distilled water.

- The electrolyte inside the battery should always cover the gridlike plates. Never overfill the battery cells with distilled water. Too much fluid can ruin a battery just as too little electrolyte can result in a dead battery. Remember that each cell is a separate unit requiring its own supply of distilled water.

- A maintenance free battery is sealed, which means you cannot add distilled water via the vent caps.

- In cold weather, never add distilled water to the cells inside the battery unless your vehicle will be driven immediately or the water will freeze and crack the battery.

- A condition indicator (an "eye") on top of the battery indicates if it is charged. Never rely completely on this indicator so also check the battery's electrolyte level by looking at the clear side of the battery.

- A battery can be load-tested to determine its ability to take and maintain a charge. Have this test performed by a professional mechanic.

- Installing electrical accessories such as a cellular phone may require upgrading to a higher-rated battery in order to handle the increased electrical usage.

- Most batteries have a lifespan of four years.

- A cracked battery may result in reduced electrical power.

- Always replace a battery with the same size and rating as the dead battery or according to your vehicle owner's manual.

- Covering the battery with a battery warmer during winter can extend its life.

- Some premium batteries incorporate a small backup battery into the main unit. A switch on top of the main battery activates a second battery. If the lights have been left on, for example, the switch can be turned on and your vehicle will start immediately, without requiring a boost. Make sure the switch is turned off once the engine has started.

Cleaning Battery Posts and Cables

- Acid buildup on the battery posts and cables prevents necessary electrical currents from flowing to and from the battery.

- To clean the battery posts of crusty white acid build-up mix 15 ml (1 tbsp.) baking soda with 250 ml (1 c.) warm water. Remove the negative cable first, then the positive cable. Use an old toothbrush to scrub the posts. As a safety precaution, always wear plastic or rubber gloves when handling a battery.

- The metal clips on the battery cables can also be cleaned using the baking soda and water mixture, but be sure the cables are completely dry before clamping them back onto the battery posts (connect the positive cable first).

- Once the posts are tightly connected to the battery cables, cover them with petroleum jelly or red-coloured battery terminal grease to prevent acid build-up.

Dead vs. Discharged Battery

- There is a difference between a dead battery and a discharged battery. A dead battery is just that – dead. It needs to be replaced. A discharged battery can be boosted or recharged using a battery charger.

- A dead battery is often the result of a cracked battery case, the plates inside the battery have disintegrated because of too many sulphates, or the plates themselves have a current leakage.

- A dead battery contains hazardous chemicals. Dispose of a dead battery by taking it to a service station.

- A discharged battery can be the result of lights left on, such as headlights or the interior light, loose battery cables, dirty battery posts and cable ends, low electrolyte levels, faulty alternator, or a loose alternator belt.

- Try not to use the electrical accessories inside your vehicle, such as the radio, if the engine isn't running as this can cause a discharged battery. If the accessories are used minimally, turn the ignition key to "accessory." This reduces electrical strain on the battery.

- To check if the battery is discharged, turn the headlights on. If the lights do not go on, the battery is probably discharged. Do the windshield wipers work? If not, the battery charge may be low.

- A discharging battery releases dangerous gases. Sometimes you can see what looks like smoke coming from the battery. These are actually gases emitted by the electrolyte as they pass through the tiny holes on top of the vent caps.

- Many accessories in your vehicle remain live even after the ignition is turned off. In a condition called "parasitic load," the battery becomes discharged if your vehicle is not driven for an extended period of time. If you anticipate not driving your vehicle for awhile, disconnect the battery cables to prevent the battery from becoming discharged.

- If the battery has been frequently discharging, always back your vehicle into the garage or parking stall. If a boost becomes necessary, your vehicle will be much easier to jumpstart in this position. Consider investing in a new battery instead of wondering whether your vehicle will start each time you get in the driver's seat.

Belts, Hoses, and Wires

Belts

Where They Are

Belts are attached to various engine components, such as the air conditioner, alternator, camshaft (a part of the engine block), crankshaft (at the bottom of the engine), power steering pump, and water pump.

What They Do

Belts work with their respective engine parts by helping transfer power.

Keeping Belts in Shape

- A belt that is not tight can easily snap when the engine is hot and revving at highway speeds.

- While your vehicle is being driven, a rock can hit a worn-out belt and break it.

- A worn-out belt appears cracked or glazed, or has exposed cords.

- Use replacement belts compatible with the make and model of your vehicle.

- When installing a new belt, replace all belts attached to the same part to provide even wear on the part.

- New belts stretch. Retighten the belt within a few of weeks of installation.

- A fan belt operates the alternator and fan, if it is not electrical.

- There should be no more than 1.3 cm ($^1/_2$ in.) play in the fan belt. If the belt is too tight, the alternator wears down quickly.

- Some fan belts have a spring tensioner that prevents the belt from slipping.

- Some vehicles have a timing belt (or chain). The timing belt is often hidden behind a plastic cover. It connects the crankshaft to the camshaft. If the timing belt breaks while the engine is running, the repairs are expensive (anything associated with the engine is a timely and costly repair).

- A belt can be the old style, "V," belt or a longer lasting serpentine belt.

Hoses

Where They Are

Major engine hoses include the upper and lower radiator hoses, a short bypass hose, and two heater hoses (one goes to the engine block and a second hose extends from the water pump). Hoses for the fuel-injection system and evaporative emissions control (EEC) are more recent additions under the hood.

What They Do

Fluids and air run through hoses and are then distributed throughout the engine.

Keeping Hoses Firm

- Hoses can be colour-coded or categorized by size. The clamps at their end connections also identify them.

- A hose should be firm and not be bulging anywhere; otherwise, it may burst.

- Fluids are most likely to leak from a hose. To extend its life, periodically wipe dirt and grease off the hose. Always keep a hose from touching other parts under the hood, especially when the engine is hot.

- Never apply firm pressure on a hose when the engine is hot as the hose could burst, especially the radiator hoses.

- Replace an old hose with a new one that is the same length, shape, and size.

- To provide even wear, replace both the upper and lower radiator hoses at the same time, even if only one hose is defective.

- The two heater hoses should "feel" the same heat when the heater is on.

- Hoses on fuel-injection systems are pressurized. Never tamper with these hoses as they could explode.

- When installing a new hose, replace their respective clamps as well.

- Fuel hoses usually have spring clamps and radiator hoses have screw clamps. Clamps on the conditioning hoses look different than clamps on these and other hoses.

- Some vehicles specify using a constant pressure spring clamp, rather than a regular screw clamp on radiator hoses.

- A hose can snap or crack from overtightening its clamp.

Wires

Where They Are

Wires extend from various engine parts, such as the spark plugs.

What They Do

Wires move electrical currents from one connection to another.

Keeping Wires Current

- Periodically clean wires of dirt, grease, and moisture accumulation. This ensures the engine components can work to their maximum efficiency.

- Wires that are cracked, frayed, or have broken strands can cause electrical shocks and reduce the electrical current running through them.

- Replace a wire with one of the same gauge or heavier.

Block (Core) Heater

Where It Is

An optional feature, the block heater is usually located between a heater hose and the engine block. One end of the block heater is plugged into the engine. The other end has a cord that plugs into an electrical outlet.

What It Does

A block heater has many advantages when plugged in. It provides additional heat to the engine, which is useful in extremely cold temperatures. In addition, a block heater helps reduce strain on the battery and starter at start-up since the engine is already warm. Engine oil also flows more easily with a warm engine.

Maximizing Use of the Block Heater

- Prior to winter, ensure that the block heater is working properly. Plug it in and you should hear a sizzling sound after a couple of minutes. Or, watch for sparks when you quickly (and safely) put the cord into and out of an electrical outlet.

- Do not leave the block heater plugged in for an extended period of time. A fire can result.

- You really only need to plug in the block heater when the temperature is colder than -15°C (+5°F).

- A block heater needs to be plugged in for only two to four hours to be effective. Plugging it in for longer wastes electricity.

- Use a power-saver cord or an outdoor timer on the block heater. Set the cord or timer two to four hours before you'll be using your vehicle.

- An extension cord longer than 8 m (26 ft.) does not carry enough electrical current for the block heater to be effective.

- When using an extension cord to plug in the block heater, use a 14 to 16 gauge wire extension cord that is grounded (it has three prongs).

- Make sure you unplug the block heater before driving away. Get into the habit of unplugging the cord before you start your vehicle.

OOOH, MY INNARDS FEEL
SO WARM AND TINGLY...

- To help keep the engine components warm while using the block heater, consider installing a battery warmer (blanket) as well.

- When having a professional mechanic install a block heater, make sure the number of watts in the block heater corresponds with the engine size.

- There are several other devices that can help keep the engine from freezing. Some examples include a heating magnet, in-line heater, in-line heater pump, interior heater, and remote starter. They attach to the block heater, lower radiator hose, or are installed inside your vehicle.

Brake Fluid and Master Cylinder

Where They Are

The brake master cylinder, which houses the brake-fluid, is usually located at the rear of the engine, near the front windshield. Brake fluid flows from the master cylinder to the wheels.

What They Do

Brake fluid works with the brake pedal to slow down or stop your vehicle by absorbing moisture and lubricating the braking system.

Braking Ground

- Most vehicles have a dual braking system, which means there are two brake fluid compartments (one for the front wheels, one for the rear) in the master cylinder.

- If your vehicle is equipped with power brakes, a power brake booster (a round unit) is attached to the brake master cylinder or it's under the floor.

- Brake fluid should be tan or clear. Change the fluid if it contains contaminants, such as dirt particles, which you'll see in the master cylinder.

- For brakes to be effective, the brake fluid level should always be 6 mm ($1/4$ in.) from the top of the reservoir.

- Air can get inside the brake lines if fluid is low or there is moisture in the brake master cylinder. If this happens, the brakes must be "bled."

- Always wipe the top of the master cylinder before opening it so that dirt particles don't fall in the cylinder and make their way through the braking system.

- Some vehicles have a clear master cylinder. This means you don't have to open the cylinder to check the fluid level.

- Brake fluid evaporates quickly. Be fast when checking the brake fluid.

- Add brake fluid slowly. If it is poured too quickly, water droplets can accumulate in the cylinder, causing rust and braking difficulties.

- Purchase small cans of brake fluid (noting if your vehicle has disc or drum brakes). An open container quickly absorbs contaminants from the air.

- Brake fluid eats paint. If any gets on your vehicle's body, wash it off with water. Never wipe it with a dry cloth.

- A silicone-based brake fluid doesn't absorb as much moisture as other, less expensive types of brake fluids.

- Sometimes, under the cover of the master cylinder is a diaphragm, a plastic or rubber sheet used to give a tight air seal for the brake fluid. Replace the diaphragm if it is cracked.

Clutch Fluid and Master Cylinder

Where They Are

On a manual transmission vehicle, the clutch fluid is housed in a master cylinder, which is usually located near the front of the engine, by the front windshield. It often sits close to the brake master cylinder.

What They Do

Clutch fluid lubricates the manual transmission gear system.

Checking the Fluid

- The clutch fluid master cylinder is smaller than the brake fluid master cylinder.

- The clutch fluid level should always be as close to the maximum mark. Never overfill the reservoir.

- The fluid in the clutch master cylinder usually uses the same fluid that sits in the brake master cylinder.

- Fluid leaks coming from anywhere around the master cylinder may disrupt ease of gear shifting.

Computer

Where It Is

The computer often sits behind the engine. Like any other computer, it consists of a memory box or computer chip.

What It Does

Most new vehicles (1986+) are equipped with a complex electronic unit (a computer) called an "electronic control module" (ECM) or "electronic control unit" (ECU). Sensors in the computer (there may be more than one computer) control various functions for systems, such as the fuel-injection and emissions.

Computer Bytes

- The computer becomes accustomed to your driving habits, such as the pressure you apply to the brake and gas pedals. When another driver gets behind the wheel, the computer must re-program itself to adapt to the new motorist.

- Because of the intricacies of the computer system, special equipment, such as a scanner, is required. A professional mechanic, then, diagnoses and services the system.

- There are at least five sensors recording and feeding information to the computer: one sensor monitors the engine coolant temperature; an oxygen (O^2) sensor measures the amount of oxygen in the exhaust system; a third sensor watches braking and traction; a fourth sensor oversees throttle position on the gas pedal; and a speed sensor observes the transmission.

- Dirt, too much heat, or vibration can affect the dependability of sensors. When a malfunction occurs, the engine can idle roughly or stall, or increased emissions results.

Emission Control Devices

Where They Are

Numerous emission control devices (three of the most common are listed below) are now part of what's under the hood. They sit in various locations throughout the engine.

What They Do

Emission control devices reduce air pollution. They also affect how smoothly an engine runs.

Evaporative Emission Control (EEC) System

- Located at the front of the engine, the EEC system has two, sometimes more, hoses extending from it.

- The EEC traps gas vapours in a canister where the fumes are burned in the engine instead of being released into the atmosphere.

Exhaust Gas Recirculation (EGR) System

- The round, metal housing EGR unit sits on the intake or exhaust manifold. It has a hose attached to it.

- The EGR redirects exhaust gases back to the engine for reburning.

- The EGR can become clogged with carbon deposits. The result is poor engine idling or stalling.

Positive Crankcase Ventilation (PCV) System

- The PCV has pipes that brings in air and recirculates gases for reburning.

- The PCV also consists of a filter and valve that are mounted near the engine.

Engine Block

Where It Is

The engine, made of cast iron or aluminum casing, is bolted together to form the main component of what's under the hood. Its largest part is the engine block (also referred to as the cylinder block), but the engine also includes the cylinder head and crankshaft. Each component has numerous parts within it, but most of them cannot be viewed unless the engine is "opened."

What It Does

All components of the casing unit (the engine) work together to ignite the engine and keep it running. The engine block and its parts require constant lubrication by the engine oil and antifreeze.

Parts of the Engine Block

Cylinder Head

> The cylinder head is bolted to the top of the engine block. Above the cylinder head sits the fuel-injection system (or carburetor).

> The combustion chambers, intake and exhaust manifolds, rocker arms, springs, and valves form part of the cylinder head.

> Usually located directly beneath the fuel-injection system (or carburetor) is the intake manifold made of steel or aluminum pipes. These pipes help regulate the air-fuel mixture.

> Even though the exhaust manifold is part of the exhaust system, it is situated at the engine, usually below the intake manifold.

> Two valves (intake and exhaust) help regulate air-fuel mixture and exhaust gases. They are attached to the camshaft, which is part of the engine block.

Engine (Cylinder) Block

> The engine block forms the largest and main part of the engine. It includes the camshaft, connecting rods, freeze-out plugs, oil galleys, pistons (or cylinders), and the water (coolant) passages.

- The camshaft is a round metal bar that sits on top of the crankshaft. A timing belt or chain links the two.
- Connecting rods join the pistons (cylinders) to the crankshaft.
- Freeze-out plugs (also called "core" or "frost" plugs) are located on the side of the engine block. Excessive pressure, due to insufficient antifreeze, causes the plugs to pop, which in turn, prevents the engine block from cracking.
- The number of pistons or cylinders corresponds to the number of spark plugs your vehicle has. For example, if it has four spark plugs, the engine block houses four pistons.
- The configuration of the engine block depends on the number of pistons (cylinders): four cylinders form one row; six cylinders form a V-shape (three on each side of the engine block); and eight cylinders also form a V-shape (four on each side).
- Water passages (or jackets) help circulate the antifreeze, which keeps the engine from overheating.
- Usually a cork gasket (called the "head gasket") sits between the cylinder head and the engine block. This gasket wears down over time, resulting in oil leaks around the engine block. A blown head gasket can also cause internal damage. Any repairs associated with the engine block are costly.
- Engine block repairs usually require a professional mechanic as special tools and equipment are needed.

Crankshaft

- The crankshaft is located at the bottom of the engine block.
- Attached to the crankshaft are the oil pan, connecting rods, a flywheel, and pistons (cylinders).
- The connecting rods can break as a result of little or no engine oil.

Engine Specifications

➤ Detailed engine particulars consist of the engine type, horsepower, and torque. Use the form in *AutoTalk Assistant* to write down the specifics on your vehicle.

➤ An example of an engine specification includes:

a) Engine type - 2.0 L, 16-valve, 4 cylinder, EFI (electronic fuel-injection)

b) Horsepower - 130 hp (94.6 kW) @ 5400 rpm

c) Torque - 114 lb./ft. (155 nm) @2400 rpm

Fuel Filter and Fuel Pump

Fuel Filter

Where It Is	What It Does
The fuel filter is located between the fuel pump and fuel-injection system (or carburetor), beside the fuel tank, or attached to the fuel pump.	Siphoning dirt particles travelling from the fuel tank serves the main function of the fuel filter.

Filtering Fuel

• A fuel filter consists of a metal, plastic, or paper pleated cylinder often held together by clamps.

• A fuel filter can become clogged, which results in the engine idling roughly.

• Most vehicles have one fuel filter although some vehicles have two. If you replace one filter, make sure you check the other one as it can be clogged as well.

• Replacing a fuel filter on a fuel-injected vehicle requires relieving pressure in the system. Usually a professional mechanic changes these fuel filters.

• Sometimes the computer system in a fuel-injected vehicle compensates for a clogged fuel filter by opening the injectors for a longer time to allow more fuel to pass through the system. The fuel filter may then become so clogged that your vehicle simply quits. If this happens, replacing the plugged fuel filter may not necessarily solve the problem as the fuel pump, which has been working overtime, quits as well.

Fuel Pump

Where It Is

The fuel pump is usually located along the fuel line, on one side of the engine block. Some fuel pumps are mounted near the fuel tank or inside it.

What It Does

A fuel pump helps move gas from the fuel tank, through the fuel lines, and then to the fuel-injection system (or carburetor).

Pumping Fuel

- There are two types of fuel pumps - electrical and mechanical. Mechanical fuel pumps, found on older vehicles, are easy to change. Most electric fuel pumps require a professional mechanic to replace them since the fuel system requires depressurization.

- An electric fuel pump helps prevent vapour locks by providing a more constant pressure to the fuel system. Vapour locks can still occur though, especially when driving at high altitudes.

- If the fuel pump is leaking, dry or wet gas streaks appear at the pump.

- A fuel pump must be replaced; it cannot be repaired.

Fuel-Injection System and Carburetor

Fuel-Injection (FI or EFI)

Where It Is

A fuel-injection (or electronic fuel-injection) system replaces the need for a carburetor. Like the carburetor, the fuel injectors sit on top of the engine. An electronic sensing device controls the amount of air and gas entering the fuel-injection system.

What It Does

The fuel-injection system works to provide sufficient fuel for a smooth running engine. Fuel injected systems also help reduce fuel consumption, lower exhaust emissions, and improve cold-starting performances.

Injecting Fuel

- Two types of fuel-injections include TBFI (throttle-body fuel-injection) and MPFI (multi-port fuel-injection). A TBFI looks the same as a carburetor, but without all the parts associated with a carburetor. A MPFI has individual injectors; the number of which corresponds to the number of cylinders your vehicle has (for example, a four-cylinder engine means there are four fuel injectors).

- The engine's computer (ECU or ECM) controls the fuel-injection system where a sensor feeds back information, such as amount and quality of air and fuel reaching the system. This sensor can become clogged, which often causes the engine to idle roughly.

- Vehicles with fuel-injection do not require servicing as often as vehicles with carburetors. But, because specific diagnostic equipment is needed, a professional mechanic should check and repair the system.

- Working on any parts of the fuel system in a fuel-injected vehicle requires depressurizing the fuel system.

- Using premium gas in a vehicle with fuel-injection helps keep the injectors clean.

- Periodically pour a bottle of fuel injector cleaning fluid into the gas tank to prevent the fuel-injection system from clogging.

Carburetor

Where It Is

A carburetor is located directly below the air cleaner, near the rear of the engine. Parts of a carburetor include the choke, which has a butterfly valve, float bowl, gas-pedal arm, idle and air-fuel adjustment screws, idle-stop solenoid, and throttle linkage.

What It Does

All parts of the carburetor work together to transform air and gas entering the carburetor into a fine mist and then distribute an appropriate amount of vapourized gas to the engine.

Not-So-Common Carburetors

- Most carburetors have an automatic choke with a butterfly valve inside the choke that opens gradually as the engine warms up. The valve should be closed when the engine is cold.

- The automatic choke, located inside the carburetor, responds to engine heat, whereas the throttle linkage, located outside the carburetor, regulates the air-fuel mixture.

- The automatic choke and throttle linkage can stick. Periodically lubricate them with small amounts of oil.

- A carburetor has one, sometimes two, adjustment screws for air-fuel mixture. They are located at the bottom of the carburetor. It also has one (sometimes two) idle screws used to regulate idling speed. These screws are also located at the bottom of the carburetor. It is important to note which screw is for idle speed and which is the air-fuel mixture adjustment screw. If the screws are covered with plugs, don't remove them to adjust the screws. Instead, have a professional mechanic look at the system.

- Some vehicles have an idle air bleed screw instead of the idle speed screw. This air bleed screw determines the amount of air entering the carburetor for proper idling.

- The gas pedal rod (or lever) located outside the carburetor may require periodic adjustment. This rod can also bend out of shape, which affects gas pedal movement.

- Some vehicles have an idle stop solenoid, a small device affixed to the side of the carburetor, which prevents the engine from continuing to idle after the ignition key is turned off. This solenoid can become defective.

Oil, Oil Filter, and Oil Pump

Oil

Where It Is

The oil dipstick is usually located on one side of the engine block, near its front. It has a curved handle that extends into a tube and then into an oil pan at the bottom of the engine.

What It Does

Engine oil lubricates engine parts. Oil also helps keep the engine cool. The dipstick is used for checking the amount and quality of engine oil in the oil pan.

Lubricating the Engine

- Make sure you are using the oil dipstick when checking engine oil and not the automatic transmission fluid dipstick. Some dipsticks have "engine oil" written on them.

- Clean oil is light brown (a honey colour). Over time, the colour changes to dark brown, then black as the oil heats up and lubricates the engine.

- If checking the oil level immediately after driving your vehicle, shut off the engine and let your vehicle sit for few minutes. This lets the oil settle back into the oil pan, providing a more accurate reading.

- To check the oil level, make sure your vehicle is on level ground. Pull out the oil dipstick, wipe it clean, reinsert it (make sure it goes all the way down to the oil pan), and then remove it again. The oil should always be between the add ("E" or "min") and full ("F" or "max") marks. Avoid overfilling the oil pan as the oil will lather and then be ineffective as a lubricant.

*AH, LUBRICATION DOES WONDERS FOR
        YOUR JOINTS !*

- On some vehicles, the oil dipstick is attached to the fill-hole cap (where the oil is added) at the top of the engine.

- The distance between the marks on the dipstick represents 1 L (1 qt.) of oil.

- When changing the oil and oil filter, keep the receipts. Your vehicle warranty is useless unless you provide proof that regular oil changes were performed using the correct weight and grade of oil.

- It is recommended you change the oil every 5,000 km (3,000 mi.), but it depends on how much city vs. highway driving is done. City driving, with its constant stops and starts, heats up and wears down engine parts more than driving for long uninterrupted periods of time. The best gauge for when to change the oil is to look at the colour and quantity of oil on the dipstick. For example, when the oil is black and at the add mark, change it, rather than adding new oil to dirty oil.

- When adding oil between oil changes, use the same weight and grade of oil already in the oil pan.

- Engine oil is rated by its thickness. Lighter grades are recommended for cold temperatures (for example, 5W30) and heavier grades for warmer weather (for example, 10W30). However, 5W30 or 10W30 is often used year-round.

- Synthetic oils offer high temperature stability and cold weather protection, which is beneficial in colder climates. Oil containers labeled "EcoLogo" mean the oil is re-refined. "Energy Conserving II" oil contains additives that improve fuel efficiency while also reducing friction on engine parts.

- The oil cap may need to be replaced, depending on the amount of sludge caked onto the inside of the cap.

- Oil leaks are common at gaskets, such as the head gasket on the engine block. Leaking oil may also be coming from around the oil pan or oil filter. The bolt at the oil pan may not be tight or the threads may be stripped, both of which result in a constant leak. If necessary, replace the bolt with a rubber suction cup.

- When changing the oil and oil filter, also grease the movable parts on the front suspension, such as ball joints and tie rod ends. This is often referred to as "greasing the nipples." Most vehicles built today have a protective rubber covering (a "boot") that permanently seals the grease on these front-end parts. However, these boots can crack or tear, causing the part to dry out.

Oil Filter

Where It Is

The oil filter, a round can with pleated paper inside, is located on the outside of the engine block, usually close to its bottom.

What It Does

The oil filter cleans impurities from the engine oil by catching these contaminants inside the filter.

Filtering Gunk

- Replace the oil filter every time you change the oil.
- The oil filter must be the correct make and size for your vehicle.

- Engine oil can leak from around the oil filter if it is not hand tightened to a snug fit. Overtightening the filter can make it difficult to remove the next time it is changed.

- An oil leak can also occur if the rubber ring on the old oil filter is not wiped off the shaft after the filter is removed. The old ring prevents the new rubber ring on the new filter from sealing the filter to the shaft.

- An oil filter can hold up to 1 L (1 qt.) of oil. When changing the oil and filter, start the engine and let it run for about 15 seconds, to circulate the oil through the filter.

Oil Pump

Where It Is

The oil pump is usually located on the side of the engine, near the oil filter and oil pan. On some vehicles, the oil pump sits inside the oil pan.

What It Does

The pump moves oil from the oil pan to the engine.

Pumping Oil

- Two types of oil pumps include gear and rotor.

- Dirty oil can cause the valve inside the oil pump to stick.

- The oil pump should not have to be changed frequently.

- An oil pump must be replaced; it cannot be repaired.

Power Steering Fluid and Pump

Where They Are

The power steering pump and the reservoir housing the power steering fluid are often located at the front of the vehicle, although some are found at the rear. There may be hoses connecting the pump to the reservoir.

What They Do

As with other fluids under the hood, power steering fluid lubricates - in this case, the steering components. The pump, driven by a belt, pressurizes the fluid so that it can move throughout the steering system.

Pumping Power

- Effective power steering fluid is clear or yellowish in colour.

- The power steering fluid dipstick usually has two "full" marks. One mark is for when the engine is hot, and the other mark is for when the engine is cold. Some reservoirs are clear so a dipstick isn't necessary.

- Generally, power steering fluid is good for the life of your vehicle.

- Overfilling the power steering fluid reservoir can damage the steering components.

- The power steering fluid cap should always be tightly secured to the reservoir so that no air gets inside.

- A power steering pump should be "quiet" when the engine is running. Unusual noises usually indicate a defective pump.

- Cracked or kinked hoses and fittings around the power steering pump inhibit the flow of fluid.

- The hoses running from the power steering pump should not touch any engine parts. Otherwise they may heat and chafe, then fail.

- A broken belt at the power steering pump means you can still control your vehicle, but the power is lost (i.e. the steering becomes manual).

Radiator and the Cooling System

Where They Are

The radiator forms part of the cooling system. It is located at the front of the engine. Additional components of the cooling system include the antifreeze (or coolant), coolant temperature sensors, fan, fan belt, freeze-out plugs, gasket, heater core, hoses and clamps, recovery tank, thermostat, and water pump. All these parts sit in different locations under the hood.

What They Do

All parts of the cooling system work together to lubricate the engine, prevent rust, dispel excess engine heat, and provide warmth to the interior of your vehicle.

Parts of the Cooling System

Antifreeze

> "Antifreeze" in *AutoTalk for Women* refers to a mixture of antifreeze fluid and water.

> Antifreeze is sometimes referred to as coolant.

> Pure antifreeze does not properly cool and protect the engine. To be effective, it must be diluted with water. Use a 50/50 or 60/40 ratio of antifreeze to water, depending on how warm or cold the temperatures get.

> Antifreeze should be good to no more than –40°C (–40°F). If the antifreeze indicates a higher number, the antifreeze gels and forms sludge.

> Flushing the old antifreeze and adding a new 50/50 or 60/40 mixture of antifreeze fluid and water helps prevent corrosion inside the radiator, as well as keeping the cooling system from overheating. Simply draining the radiator and refilling it with new antifreeze does not remove all the old antifreeze from the entire system.

> Maintain the antifreeze level approximately 5 cm (2 in.) below the radiator cap.

> Antifreeze should always be "clean and green" (or reddish). Old antifreeze shows itself as jelly and corrodes the insides of the radiator.

➤ Antifreeze leaks can occur while your vehicle is being driven. The leak may not necessarily show up as a fluid spill underneath your stationary vehicle.

➤ Not only is antifreeze poisonous to taste, it also has a toxic smell. This odour can seep inside your vehicle if there is an antifreeze leak.

➤ A fire can result if antifreeze is spilled onto any hot engine parts.

➤ Use antifreeze all year-round, even in the hot summer months.

Coolant Temperature Sensors

➤ Two coolant temperature sensors, one in the radiator and the other at the engine block, indicate, via the temperature gauge on the dashboard, if the engine is overheating.

➤ The sensor units can malfunction, causing an inaccurate reading on the temperature gauge.

Fan and Fan Belt

➤ The fan and fan belt are usually located directly behind the radiator.

➤ The fan regulates airflow through the radiator.

➤ The fan can be either electrical or belt driven, although a clutch fan is often found on vehicles with air conditioning.

➤ An electrical fan is sometimes attached to the radiator and is regulated by a motor and temperature switch. This type of fan can start turning when the engine is hot, but the ignition is off.

➤ A mechanical fan has plastic or metal blades and is driven by a belt. This belt is also attached to the water pump.

➤ Bent or broken fan blades can cause the water pump to fail.

Freeze-Out Plugs

➤ Freeze-out plugs (or "core" or "frost" plugs) are small, round discs located on the side of the engine block, usually below the spark plugs. They are difficult to see and reach because of their location.

➤ Freeze-out plugs prevent the engine block from cracking due to excessive pressure, which can be caused by frozen antifreeze.

➤ For freeze-out plugs to be effective, replace any that are corroded.

➤ Antifreeze can leak from a freeze-out plug, which is evident by rust around the plug.

➤ Using a stop-leak additive can sometimes seal leaks around the freeze-out plugs.

Gaskets

➤ Gaskets seal two metal parts together to prevent fluid leaks, such as antifreeze (and oil).

➤ A gasket can't be seen unless the two metal parts are taken apart.

➤ Gaskets are found in a number of locations throughout the engine, such as at the engine block (between the cylinder head and engine block), thermostat, and water pump.

➤ There are often two gaskets at the thermostat. If one cracks, antifreeze tends to leak from around the thermostat.

➤ There is usually one large gasket between the water pump and the engine. Antifreeze dripping from around the water pump could mean this gasket is cracked, not that the water pump is faulty.

➤ Gasket sealers are coated on new gaskets to firmly seal the gasket to the metal part.

Heater Core and Heater Control Valve

➤ The heater *core* is usually located under the dashboard or at the back of the engine, near the front windshield. The heater control *valve* is mounted along one of the heater hoses running from the engine block to the heater core. Both the heater core (a miniature radiator) and heater valve (a one way passage) control the flow of antifreeze, which supplies heat to the interior of your vehicle.

➤ A blower motor (or electric fan), mounted on the heater core, helps regulate the flow of heat into the interior of your vehicle by way of the ventilation outlets. This motor can burn-out.

➤ Some vehicles have more than two heater hoses.

➤ Heater hoses are usually the same diameter, but some engines are equipped with hoses of different sizes.

➤ The heater hoses should "feel" the same temperature when the heater is on.

➤ A liquid sealant can be used to repair heater leaks. However, the entire heater unit usually must be replaced.

Radiator

➤ A radiator sits at the front of the engine. Extending from the radiator are two hoses, one lower and one upper.

➤ The pressurized radiator houses antifreeze. Once the engine is running, antifreeze circulates inside the radiator and moves to other parts of the cooling system.

➤ The outside of the radiator core should be black or grey. Green along the seams and fins indicates rust or antifreeze leaks.

➤ The bolts attached to the radiator should be tight; otherwise, the core can become damaged by vibration or from being hit by the fan.

➤ Most radiators have a drain plug (called a "petcock") at the bottom of the radiator used to drain antifreeze. The plug must be tight, or a slow antifreeze leak will result. Turn it clockwise to tighten, counterclockwise to loosen.

➤ Leaking from the radiator core means its insides are corroded and rusted out. Replace the radiator, rather than repair it.

➤ Using a stop-leak additive in the radiator can sometimes seal an antifreeze leak, but it provides a temporary seal only. Always follow the directions on the can.

➤ The exterior of the radiator core, especially after a long trip in spring or summer, often has dead bugs and leaves stuck to it. This debris interferes with air circulation to and from the radiator. Clean the front of the radiator when the engine is cold by spray washing the core with water.

➤ Never remove the radiator cap when the engine is warm or hot or the antifreeze in the radiator may explode, causing serious burns to your hands or face.

➤ Remove the radiator cap in a counterclockwise direction, at an angle, and never have your body directly over it. As an added precaution, wear gloves. Some radiator caps have a lever to relieve pressure before it is removed. Sometimes, the cap is located on the antifreeze recovery tank.

➤ Overtightening the radiator cap can cause antifreeze inside the radiator to explode from too much pressure.

➤ The radiator should have a manufacturer-approved radiator cap with the appropriate pressure limit.

➤ Loose or broken springs on the radiator cap can result in too little pressure inside the radiator. Tears or cracks in the radiator cap's rubber ring (seal) indicate a faulty cap.

Recovery Tank

➤ The recovery tank is also referred to as the "antifreeze recovery" or the "coolant recovery" tank.

➤ The see-through plastic recovery tank is usually located on one side of the engine. A small rubber hose connects it to the radiator.

➤ The hose extending from the recovery tank to the radiator can get plugged, which means the recovery tank is not an accurate indication of the antifreeze level. A more accurate way to check is to open the radiator cap (when the engine is cold) and look at the amount of antifreeze in the radiator.

➤ Once you are sure the hose from the recovery tank is not plugged, maintain the antifreeze in the recovery tank between the appropriate marks, noting which is for when the antifreeze is hot and which is for when it's cold. Never overfill the tank.

➤ If the hose extending from the recovery tank leaks or is plugged, replace both it and its clamps.

➤ If adding antifreeze to the recovery tank, make sure you do not mistake the windshield-washer reservoir for the antifreeze recovery tank. Both are plastic and are often beside one another, but the antifreeze recovery tank usually has a small hose running from the top of the cap to let any overflowing antifreeze escape.

➤ Some recovery tanks are pressurized, which means the engine must be cool before the reservoir cap can be opened.

Thermostat

➤ The thermostat controls the temperature of the antifreeze.

➤ A thermostat is not visible because it sits inside a housing unit called the "water outlet," which is connected to one end of the upper radiator hose.

➤ Most thermostats are all-season, which means they have summer and winter settings that adjust automatically. Some thermostats are designated winter and summer, which means a new thermostat has to be installed for each season.

➤ A defective thermostat cannot be repaired; it must be replaced.

➤ The water outlet unit that holds the thermostat may require replacing if antifreeze leaks occur around it.

Water Pump

➤ The water pump is most often located near the fan, at the front of the engine. It can also be located on one side of the engine block.

➤ A water pump cannot be seen unless the fan is removed.

➤ The water pump's main function is to circulate and cool antifreeze.

➤ The lower radiator hose connects the water pump to the radiator.

➤ A water pump cannot be repaired; it must be replaced. A stop-leak additive will not stop a water pump from leaking.

➤ An antifreeze leak may be the result of a cracked gasket at the water pump, rather than a faulty water pump.

Spark Plugs, Spark Plug Wires, and the Ignition System

Where They Are

Located on the engine (cylinder) block, spark plugs and their wires form part of the vehicle's ignition system. Wires extend from the spark plugs to the ignition system.

What They Do

Spark plugs and the ignition system work together with the alternator, battery, and starter to ignite the air-fuel mixture in the engine and keep it running smoothly.

Spark Plugs

• The number of spark plugs indicates the type of engine. For example, four spark plugs means your vehicle has a four-cylinder engine.

• The electrodes at the end of each spark plug should be square when new. Under normal driving conditions, spark plugs should wear down in a curved manner, with the colour of carbon deposits being light brown or grey.

• Use the brand and model of spark plug recommended by your vehicle's manufacturer.

• In most cases, install new spark plugs instead of cleaning and regapping the used plugs. Use the old spark plugs as spares.

- Replace spark plugs in complete sets, rather than only one or two at a time.

- Never install a spark plug too tightly or hold the socket incorrectly. The spark plug may break at midpoint while being installed or removed.

- Ensure all spark plugs are properly gapped. If just one is improperly gapped, the engine will idle roughly.

- Constant city driving (lots of stops and starts) leads to heavy carbon build-up on the spark plugs. Too much carbon on the electrodes results in the engine idling roughly or stalling.

Spark Plug Wires

- You can tell how many cylinders your vehicle has by counting the number of spark plug wires extending from the engine block. Be sure to look on both sides of the engine.

- There is lots of electricity passing through spark plug wires. Be careful when touching the wires while the engine is running.

- Spark plug wires must be attached to their appropriate spark plug. An incorrect firing order can cause the engine to stall or not start at all.

- Avoid pulling a spark plug wire from the middle. Pull it from its "boot" (end).

- Replace spark plug wires with ones having the same length and thickness at the ends.

- Consider replacing spark plug wires when installing new spark plugs so that electricity flows evenly through all the plugs.

- When installing spark plug wires, replace them one at a time, to avoid getting them mixed up. Some wire sets are numbered to identify where they should be attached.

Ignition System

- There are three types of ignition systems - breaker-point ignitions (distributors), breakerless ignition systems, and electronic ignition systems (the most common systems on vehicles built today).

- A breaker-point ignition system uses a distributor, which consists of a black or blue plastic cap, a pick-up coil, and a rotor. A breakerless ignition uses an electronic switch. The electronic system uses a computer to work the ignition system.

- Hairline cracks on the distributor cap can cause the engine to idle roughly.

- Replace a defective distributor cap with one recommended by the vehicle manufacturer.

- To clean the distributor cap, remove the clips or screws around it. With a dry cloth, wipe the inside of the cap, especially around the carbon and metal contacts. Make sure the spark plug wires stay on their corresponding tower atop the distributor cap.

- Other parts of the ignition system, such as the pick-up coil, may require periodic adjustment or replacement.

Starter

Where It Is

The starter is an electric motor powered by the battery. It is usually located at the bottom and side of the crankshaft. One end of the battery cable is attached to the starter and starter solenoid.

What It Does

The starter's electrical current, running from the battery, starts the engine once the ignition key is turned to "on."

Getting Started

- The starter is connected to a starter solenoid. This starter solenoid should never be adjusted or replaced unless it malfunctions.

- Release the ignition key as soon as the engine starts; otherwise, the starter overheats and may burn out.

- If any of the components inside the starter become defective, the entire motor must be replaced.

- The starter motor is going bad when it grinds as the engine is started.

- Engine oil can contaminate the starter. Be careful not to get oil on the starter, especially when changing the oil and oil filter.

Windshield-Washer Reservoir

Where It Is

The windshield-washer reservoir is usually located on one side of the engine, near the front. It is a white plastic container that often has a picture of a windshield with squirting water on the top. The reservoir also has a hose extending from it, and is equipped with a pump operated by a motor.

What It Does

The reservoir holds winter or summer windshield-washer fluid, which helps keep your vehicle's front (and back) windows clean and free of obstructions.

Washing Windows

- Windshield-washer fluid is either pink (summer fluid) or blue (winter fluid).

- Summer windshield-washer solution contains chemicals that remove dead bugs and other seasonal grime.

- Winter windshield-washer solution has properties that prevent it from freezing and cracking the reservoir in cold temperatures.

- Adding antifreeze to the windshield-washer reservoir can result in paint damage to the body of your vehicle.

- Never fill the washer fluid to the top of the reservoir since fluid expands as the temperature increases. Always leave 2.5 to 5 cm (1 to 2 in.) at the top.

AH, NEW WASHER FLUID. IT'S ALL GONNA BE CLEAR TO ME NOW!

- The hose at the reservoir often twists. To avoid losing solution or having the washer unit malfunction, replace the hose if it becomes cracked or brittle.

- Dirt can clog the reservoir hose. To clean, flush with warm water.

- The filter screen at the bottom of the reservoir can rip or become corroded. Replace this part, rather than trying to clean it.

Section 4
Underneath Your Vehicle

This section looks underneath your vehicle. Starting at the front are the brakes, oil pan, suspension system, and transmission. The exhaust system, with all its pipes and other parts, makes its way from the front to the back of your vehicle. Rear brakes, fuel tank, and the rear suspension system sit at the back of your vehicle.

For specific information on what's underneath your car or multi-purpose vehicle (minivan, light truck, or sport-utility vehicle), consult the owner's manual.

SECTION FOUR CONTENTS

...cont'd

Introduction

The parts situated underneath your vehicle are often overlooked. But, there are many pipes, pans, and other components vital to the overall running of your automobile. To get an overview of these components, you'll have to crawl underneath your vehicle. A more practical, and cleaner, solution is for you to take a tire off its wheel and then secure your vehicle on a hydraulic hoist. At this vantage point, you are able to see more clearly the pipes running from front to back and all that's in-between. It's also easier to look at all the suspension parts with one tire off its wheel.

Turn the pages to discover more about what's underneath your vehicle and how to keep everything in good working condition.

Brakes

- Vehicles built today are equipped with a dual hydraulic braking system, which means the front and rear wheels brake independently of one another. Brakes should never fully fail with this dual braking system.

- There are two types of brakes: disc brakes and drum brakes. The braking systems operating these brakes use a conventional or an anti-lock braking system (ABS).

- Before checking the brakes, lightly spray water them to settle down brake dust.

- A brake job can involve installing new linings, replacing calipers, wheel cylinders, drums and rotors, springs, and bleeding the system. Or, in a term called "machining the rotors," the rotors are filed and smoothed out and then re-installed on your vehicle.

- Bleeding the brakes removes air from the brake system. Once the lines are bled, fresh fluid is pumped through them. Since special tools are required to bleed the system, this procedure is usually left to a professional mechanic.

- A power brake booster is located between the brake pedal and the brake master cylinder. This booster makes it easier for you to press down on the brake pedal.

Anti-lock Brake System (ABS)

- Vehicles with anti-lock brakes have them on all four wheels, or on the two front wheels only. In trucks, anti-lock brakes can be on all four wheels, or the rear wheels only.

- An ABS means a computer relies on sensors to regulate the amount of pressure applied to the brakes.

- Under normal braking conditions, the ABS is *not* activated. Its sensors work only when there is excessive braking force.

- Anti-lock brakes work faster than conventional brakes. They are designed to keep the tires from skidding because the wheels don't lock up. This helps you stay in control of your vehicle when a sudden stop is necessary.

- Having anti-lock brakes does not mean you can stop without skidding. On ice-, slush-, and snow-covered roads, you can skid. The difference is in *how* you brake.

- If you need to quickly stop, apply firm and constant pressure on the brake pedal. This prevents the wheels from locking and allows you to stay in control of your steering. Never pump anti-lock brakes as this nullifies the anti-lock brake system.

- Anti-lock brakes often result in a rapid pulsation on the brake pedal when the system is activated. Other ABS brake pedal movements include the pedal periodically dropping or feeling "hard." Become familiar with the anti-lock braking characteristics on your vehicle. Practise using the ABS in an empty parking lot by safely braking at 30 km/h (20 mph). Test your ABS under various road conditions, such as ice and snow.

Disc Brakes

- Disc brakes are common on the front wheels, although some vehicles have disc brakes on all four wheels. They are never on just the rear wheels.

- Parts of a disc brake include the brake pad, caliper, and disc (or rotor). Disc brakes also have a brake pad wear indicator (or sensor) on the pad. If you hear a metallic sound when applying the brakes, the indicator is letting you know the pads are worn down to the point where they must be replaced.

- Disc brake pads are usually smaller than drum brake shoes, which means they wear down faster.

- Each brake pad should be thicker than 1.6 mm ($^1/_{16}$ in.) for minimum braking ability.

- Disc brakes usually last 30,00 to 45,000 km (18,000 to 28,000 miles).

- A disc brake automatically adjusts to the wearing down of the pad.

- Always replace disc brakes in pairs.

- A cracked disc is a safety hazard. Scratches on the disc also reduce braking effectiveness.

Drum Brakes

- Drum brakes sit on the rear wheels.

- Parts of a drum brake include the adjusting nut, brake shoes, brake linings, drum, springs, and wheel cylinder.

- The wheel cylinder forces the brake shoes against the drum, which stops your vehicle. This cylinder can sometimes crack.

- Scratches or cracks on the drum surrounding the brake shoes, brake linings, and wheel cylinder can affect braking ability.

- Most vehicles have self-adjusting retractable springs located inside the drum, which automatically moves the shoes closer to the drum. If you need to manually adjust the brake shoes, there are two options. One is to hit the brake pedal hard when driving at a slow speed in "R." Be safety conscious when doing this adjustment. The second option is to park your vehicle on level ground and remove the rubber plug at the back of the wheel. Locate the adjusting nut using a flathead screwdriver and rotate the nut.

- A drum brake shoe should be thicker than 1.6 mm ($^1/_{16}$ in.) for minimum braking effectiveness.

- Drum brakes usually last 40,000 to 60,000 km (24,000 to 37,000 mi.).

- Always replace drum brakes in pairs.

- When changing drum brakes, never depress the brake pedal or engage/disengage the parking brake as damage to the braking system can result.

Brake Hoses and Brake Lines

Brake Hoses

➤ Brake (flex) hoses are located behind each tire and run from the brakes to the brake lines.

➤ Oil, road grime, cracks, or leaks on any of the brake hoses can cause braking difficulties.

➤ Hoses for both the front and back brakes can crack at the same time, resulting in no brake fluid reaching any of the brakes. Because all braking power is lost, use the parking brake to stop your vehicle.

➤ Install brake hoses without twisting the hoses.

Brake Lines

➤ Brake lines lead from the brake master cylinder and are attached to a rubber hose at each tire.

➤ Cracked brake lines can cause brake fluid to leak, which is evident in streaks of dried or wet fluid along the brake lines or on the hoses.

Exhaust System

Catalytic Converter

- The catalytic converter is located between the exhaust manifold and the muffler (or resonator).

- A catalytic converter collects exhaust gases and moves them out through the exhaust and tailpipes.

- The catalytic converter reduces pollution, but it does not prevent carbon monoxide from possibly entering the interior of your vehicle or being emitted into the air.

- If your vehicle is equipped with a catalytic converter, you should use unleaded gas. Leaded gas damages the inside of the converter.

- Catalytic converters get very hot and it takes them a long time to cool down. Never park your vehicle in grass, small bush, or around other combustible material.

Exhaust Manifold

- The exhaust manifold is located at the engine, usually below the intake manifold.

- Some manifolds are constructed of stainless steel, which extends its life. They also have a series of pipes that re-route exhaust gases.

- Worn gaskets on the manifold often cause exhaust leaks.

Muffler, Tailpipe and Other Pipes

- The *head pipe* is the pipe that extends from the exhaust manifold to the catalytic converter. The *exhaust pipe* runs from the catalytic converter to the muffler. The *tailpipe* extends from the muffler.

- Exhaust components tend to rust from back to front, which is why the tailpipe and muffler are the most frequently changed parts of the exhaust system.

- Shake the tailpipe when the engine is cold to check if there are any loose clamps or hangers.

- If there are rust spots on the muffler's exterior, tap them with a screwdriver. If it pushes a hole through the rust, it's time to replace the muffler.

- Tap the muffler with a wrench or hammer. A clear ringing is normal, whereas a dull thud indicates the internal chambers are rusting or have collapsed.

- Installing a new muffler can also mean replacing the exhaust pipe if they are one unit. Rather than paying for the entire assembly, have your mechanic fit an adapter onto the muffler so that a new exhaust pipe doesn't have to be installed.

- Some vehicles have a resonator as well as a muffler. The resonator works with the muffler to reduce noise.

LOOKS LIKE MY REAR END COULD USE AN UPLIFT !!

Clamps and Hangers

- Loose clamps or broken or stretched hangers often cause pipes to leak exhaust fumes. They can also result in pipes and other exhaust parts making a rattling sound.

- When replacing clamps and hangers, use the same size as the old ones. Installation will be easier than trying to fit smaller or larger clamps and hangers onto the exhaust part.

- Once new clamps are installed and after you have driven your vehicle for awhile, re-tighten the clamps.

This Is Exhausting!

- Carbon monoxide is a silent killer. Loose or rusty components in the exhaust system can cause carbon monoxide fumes to leak out. If this odourless gas seeps inside your vehicle, you may feel drowsy or nauseous, you get a headache, and/or you hear a ringing in your ears.

- The pipes on the exhaust system are often a darker color than the other metal parts under the hood. Engine pipes are usually reddish-brown.

- Some vehicles have a dual exhaust system (for example, two catalytic converters, two mufflers, and two tailpipes). Other vehicles' exhaust systems are one large section. This means that if the muffler needs replacing, the entire rear section must be replaced.

- Rain, snow, road salt, and alkaline (a rusting agent) all contribute to rust throughout the exhaust system. A stainless steel exhaust system prevents excessive rust from happening.

COUGH! COUGH!

Fuel Tank

- Inside the fuel tank is an electronic sending unit that corresponds with the arrow on the gas gauge on the dashboard. This unit can become defective.

- Sometimes fuel at gas stations is contaminated, which can cause the engine to idle roughly.

- A full tank of gas adds weight, which provides extra traction to your vehicle.

- Periodically tighten the hangers or straps supporting the fuel tank.

- Holes (including pinholes) in the fuel tank, wet spots around the seams of the tank, and dents on the fuel tank can all lead to an explosion.

- If your fuel tank is constantly low in gas, sediment at the bottom of the tank enters the fuel line, which often clogs the fuel filter. Water vapours also form inside the tank and along the fuel line. In both cases, the engine may idle roughly or stall.

- Pouring gas-line antifreeze into the fuel tank prevents water droplets from turning into ice crystals, but it does not melt ice already formed inside the tank or along the fuel line. By maintaining a full fuel tank, especially in cold temperatures, moisture doesn't have a place to accumulate.

Oil Pan

- The oil pan houses engine oil. It is bolted to the bottom of the crankshaft (below the engine block), towards the front of your vehicle.

- The oil dipstick extends from the top of the engine and goes into the oil pan. The dipstick indicates the amount and quality of engine oil sitting in the pan.

- The oil pan has a drain plug that loosens counterclockwise and tightens clockwise.

- When changing engine oil, clean the drain hole threads before reinserting the drain plug. This helps prevent the threads from stripping.

- Sometimes the drain hole threads wear down, making it difficult to use the drain plug without oil constantly dripping. If the threads are stripped, insert a rubber suction-type oil plug, rather than using a brass, screw-on plug.

Suspension System

- The suspension system consists of the front suspension, driveshaft, rear suspension, shock absorbers, springs, and the stabilizer bar(s).

- These suspension parts help to hold the weight of your vehicle, cargo, and all passengers, while also providing a smooth, safe, and stable ride.

- To quickly inspect the suspension system, have someone sit in the driver's seat when your vehicle is on level ground and all tires are properly inflated. If there is sagging at any of its four corners, some suspension parts may be loose or worn-out.

- Repairing the suspension system requires a professional mechanic as special tools and equipment are required.

Front Suspension

- Parts of the front suspension include ball joints, CV-joints (constant velocity joints), control arms, shock absorbers or struts, springs, stabilizer bar, tie rods, and tie rod ends.

- Most vehicles are equipped with independent front suspension. This means that each wheel on the same axle, while attached to the front of your vehicle, is independent of the other.

- Independent front suspension provides a more comfortable ride, especially over bumps and holes. Its suspension also allows more ease in steering.

- With your vehicle on level ground and the engine not running, wiggle each tire back and forth using both hands. Excessive movement often indicates loose or worn-out front-end suspension parts.

Ball Joints

➤ Upper and lower ball joints are located on the upper and lower control arms, behind each front wheel.

➤ Ball joints allow the front wheels to move up and down and side to side. All ball joints should have similar horizontal and vertical play. If there is too much play, the ball joint probably needs to be replaced.

➤ Most ball joints have a lifetime lubrication, which means that the grease on the nipples is covered in a rubber-housing unit. This unit can crack, though, which causes the grease to dry out.

CV-Joints (Constant Velocity Joints)

➤ CV-joints are usually found at each front wheel. They are common on front wheel drive vehicles.

➤ CV-joints are unique U- joints (universal joints) in that they move in all directions. This helps maintain vehicle stability.

➤ CV-joints have grease-packed ball bearings. Sealed around them are rubber boots that can sometimes tear, causing the bearings to dry out.

Control Arms

➤ Usually there are two control arms (upper and lower) attached to the front wheel spindle.

➤ Control arms assist in ease of steering.

➤ Most passenger vehicles are now built with strut mounted assemblies. These connections to the vehicle's body replace the upper control arm and upper ball joint.

Struts

➤ Struts have the same function as shock absorbers. As well as helping with your vehicle's up and down movement, struts influence vehicle control, wheel alignment, and tire wear.

➤ A strut is either rebuildable or non-rebuildable. A rebuildable strut is just that – a new shock cartridge is installed by removing a nut. A non-rebuildable strut is sealed so the entire assembly must be replaced.

➤ MacPherson struts, a special type of shock absorber, combine the shock absorber and spring into one unit. This makes for improved road handling and stability.

➤ Strut mount assemblies wear out over time, causing your vehicle to pull towards the last direction it was turned. This is referred to as "memory steering."

➤ When having a professional mechanic check the strut mount assembly on your vehicle, have her or him look for radial or axial movement exceeding the specifications outlined in your vehicle owner's manual. Look for cracks in the rubber or if the rubber has separated from the steel portion of the strut mount.

➤ If the front struts are replaced, the front wheels need to be realigned.

➤ Sport-utility vehicles are particularly prone to strut mount wear. The added weight of these vehicles puts that much more pressure on the strut mounts.

Tie Rods and Tie Rod Ends

➤ Tie rods are ball and socket devices that assist the steering system in stabilizing vehicle movement.

➤ On each wheel, there is usually one inner and one outer tie rod end.

➤ Tie rod ends may require periodic lubrication if they are not equipped with rubber seals. The rubber seal can dry out and crack, though, causing the grease to dry out.

Rear Suspension

• Rear suspension differs from front suspension in that the weight displacement is more varied at the rear due to passenger weight in the rear seat, cargo in the trunk, etc. Rear wheels are also more rigid than front wheels because they are often attached to an axle that has a rear differential in the middle. Like the front wheels, though, rear wheels have shock absorbers, springs, and sometimes a stabilizer bar.

Rear Differential

➤ Only RWD (rear wheel drive), 4WD (four wheel drive), or all-wheel drive vehicles are equipped with a rear differential.

➤ A rear differential lets the back wheels turn at different speeds.

➤ A driveshaft runs from the rear differential to the front of the vehicle. Along the driveshaft is a U-joint (universal joint).

➤ Sometimes the rear differential and the axle (the rod joining the two rear wheels) are called the "rear end."

➤ The rear differential has a gearbox that contains fluid to lubricate bearings, gears, and shafts.

➤ The gearbox usually has two plugs: a *filler* plug located at the side and a *drain* plug at the bottom.

➤ To get an accurate reading of the fluid level in the rear differential, make sure your vehicle is on level ground. Remove the filler plug. If fluid drips out, the rear differential is probably okay.

➤ If the fluid level is low, add a lubricant recommended in the vehicle owner's manual.

➤ The rear differential usually becomes damaged as a result of low fluid or your vehicle is driven with too heavy a load at its rear end.

U-Joints (Universal Joints)

➤ U-joints are found only on rear wheel and four wheel drive vehicles.

➤ U-joints are attached to the driveshaft at both ends.

➤ U-joints should be able to perform a flexing motion (like ball joints), except there is no side to side movement. Excessive play between the driveshaft and U-joint usually indicates a faulty U-joint.

➤ Most U-joints are sealed with boots to keep grease inside them.

Shock Absorbers

• Shock absorbers are attached to your vehicle's frame and its suspension arms.

• Shock absorbers help soften the up and down movement when your vehicle is driven.

• There are shock absorbers for all wheels, not only the front.

• Types of shock absorbers include gas-powered, heavy-duty, and variable-load.

• Bolts hold the shock in place, at the top and bottom.

• Replace the shocks in pairs (two in the front or two in the rear).

- To check if the shock absorbers are losing their capabilities, lean against one corner of the hood and bounce your vehicle. If your vehicle keeps bouncing after you have stopped, the shock at that corner is probably worn-out. Perform this bounce test at all four corners.

- Shocks show a small amount of fluid. Excessive oil on a shock indicates that the seal is old and the shock needs to be replaced.

- Worn-out shock absorbers affect tire tread. Bumps across the tire is one indication the shock absorber at that corner may be defective.

Springs

- Springs are situated between each wheel (both front and rear) and are mounted between the control arms.

- Springs are beside the shock absorber or, as with MacPherson struts, wrapped around the shock absorbers.

- There are three types of springs: coil, leaf, and torsion. Each type helps a vehicle absorb road bumps (along with the shocks), maintain a level balance in turning situations, and provide for a quiet ride.

Stabilizer Bars

- Stabilizer bars can be found at the front and rear of your vehicle.

- A stabilizer bar connects the suspension system on the two front wheels. If a stabilizer bar is at the back of your vehicle, it connects the two rear wheels.

- Stabilizer bars help keep your vehicle level, especially in turns. They also soften the side to side movement.

Kinds of Drive Systems

Front Wheel Drive Vehicles (FWD)

- ➤ A front wheel drive vehicle combines the transmission and differential into one unit called a transaxle. The transaxle sits beside the engine block.

- ➤ A transaxle connects the front wheels to the steering wheel, giving all the power to the front.

- ➤ Having the transaxle at the front makes it heavier, which improves traction, especially on slippery roads.

- ➤ Many front wheel drive vehicles utilize a strut type of front suspension system.

Rear Wheel Drive Vehicles (RWD)

➤ A rear wheel drive vehicle has a long driveshaft that connects the differential, located on the rear axle between the two back wheels, to the steering wheel.

➤ The driveshaft is usually attached on both sides by U-joints.

➤ The driveshaft and rear differential send power only to the rear wheels.

➤ The differential lets the rear wheels move at different speeds when turning a corner.

Four Wheel Drive Vehicles

➤ Four wheel drive vehicles are configured like rear wheel drive vehicles in that a driveshaft connects the differential to the steering wheel.

➤ An additional part to these vehicles is the transfer case, which gives power to all four wheels.

➤ A shift lever is usually by the driver's seat. When activated, it locks together the front and rear axles, shifting the vehicle into a four-wheel drive.

➤ Having a four wheel drive increases traction, especially on gravel, ice-, and snow-covered roads.

All Wheel Drive Vehicles

➤ These vehicles are also called full-time four wheel drives.

➤ Power is given to all four wheels at all times so that no shifting is required.

➤ As with four wheel drive vehicles, all-wheel drive vehicles improve movement on all dry and wet road surfaces.

Transmissions

Automatic Transmission

• The automatic transmission and the pan holding the reddish-pink transmission fluid are often located towards the middle underside of the engine, behind the oil pan.

- Many automatic transmissions are now computer controlled to shift gears depending on how much pressure is put on the gas pedal.

- Most damage to the transmission occurs when your vehicle is cold and there has been no time to heat the transmission fluid. This is why the engine should run for a minute before shifting the gear to "D." Always drive away slowly, rather than "putting the pedal to the metal."

- How often the transmission fluid needs to be replaced depends on where your vehicle has been driven. If, for example, your vehicle has pulled a trailer or been through a lot of dust or water, stress on the transmission and contaminants getting inside the pan have probably affected the quality of fluid.

- If a professional mechanic replaces the automatic transmission, make sure all bolts are sufficiently tightened. If they aren't, you might hear a constant rattling, which means a return visit to your mechanic.

- Some vehicles have sealed transmission units, while others have a drain plug. The bolt on this plug is usually larger than the bolt on the engine oil pan.

Manual Transmission

- The manual transmission gears and other parts, including the pan, are located directly below the gearshift or near the engine.

- Parts of the transmission include the clutch disc, flywheel, pressure plate bearing, and the throw-out bearing.

- The manual transmission pan has dark sticky transmission fluid used to lubricate the gears and other parts. There are two plugs on the pan, a metal or rubber *inspection* (or filler) plug attached to its side and the *drain* plug affixed to its underside.

- To check the fluid level in the manual transmission pan, remove the filler plug. If fluid comes out, the level is fine. No fluid coming out could mean worn-out parts.

- If you must add manual transmission fluid, use a lubricant specified in your vehicle owner's manual.

- Water can enter the manual transmission pan, especially if your vehicle has been driven through deep water.

Section 5
Troubleshooting

Your vehicle makes unexpected whines, squeaks, and knocks no matter how well maintained it is. This section explores the reasons for these and other unusual noises made under the hood, in and around the tires, and underneath your vehicle. *Troubleshooting* also suggests causes for particular sights and smells. Many unfamiliar sights, smells, sounds, and how your vehicle feels as it moves indicate potential engine failure and present safety concerns. When trouble occurs, take your vehicle to a professional mechanic, to the nearest gas station, or into a reputable automotive service centre.

"Scenarios – What to Do" offers advice on some all-to-common situations, such as a flat tire and skidding. If you are driving in adverse weather conditions, precautions are necessary to ensure you're protected. In all these cases, you want to "shoot the trouble" and resume driving in confidence, comfort, and safety.

For specific information on troubleshooting your car or multi-purpose vehicle (minivan, light truck, or sport-utility vehicle), consult the owner's manual.

SECTION FIVE CONTENTS

...cont'd

Introduction

When an unexpected driving situation occurs, it's important not to panic. In many cases, common sense prevails. Do what you need to do to solve the problem, which all depends on factors, such as where you are, what time of day it is, who your passengers are, how much time you have, and your knowledge of the mechanics of your vehicle. Your most effective initial course of action is to pull safely over to the side of the road. From there, you can assess the situation.

Knowing your vehicle is imperative to troubleshooting. Familiarize yourself with what makes your vehicle move. With recent innovations, such as anti-lock brakes, vehicles are much more diversified depending on their make and model. Get to know the specific characteristics of your vehicle and how they affect performance and reliability.

Knowledge of basic automotive supplies and tools will also assist you in diagnosing and sometimes resolving a problem. Start by acquainting yourself with booster cables, lug wrench, screwdrivers, and wrenches. Then, when you are ready for tackling an unforeseen repair, you are armed with the necessary tools.

Prevention is the key to alleviating vehicle malfunctions and failures. A guide to preventive care is found in the beginning pages of *Behind the Wheel.*

Here are a few tips to keep in mind when troubleshooting:

> ➤ North American standards look at the left side of a vehicle as the driver's side and the right side of a vehicle as the passenger side. Mechanics often refer to the left and right side when discussing engine and other parts.

> ➤ A general rule of thumb when loosening and tightening bolts and clamps is that turning left loosens and turning right tightens. In other words – lefty loosey, righty tighty.

> ➤ Be extra cautious when looking under the hood while the engine is running. For example, remove long necklaces and jewellrey, such as rings and watches, and tie back long hair.

> ➤ Smoking around an open hood with the engine idling is dangerous. A spark could ignite, resulting in a fire.

> ➤ Most fluids you put into your vehicle are poisonous. Try not to get any on your hands. If you do, wash them immediately. To avoid having this happen, wear gloves and keep your hands away from your face, especially the eyes.

➤ Carbon monoxide fumes are deadly. Be aware of how they can easily seep into the interior of your vehicle. Take the necessary precautions to ensure your vehicle is not at risk.

➤ If you must check hoses, tires, and other engine parts when they are hot, use the back of your hand, rather than the palm. Muscles in the palm cause it to close around the heat source, whereas muscles in the back of the hand pull away from heat.

➤ Always put back engine parts in the reverse order they were taken out. Draw a sketch or take an instant Polaroid to help you remember.

➤ Label wires, hoses, and other parts when removing them. This makes it much easier to put the part back in its correct location, rather than relying on memory alone.

➤ If your vehicle is disabled on the side of a highway and you must go for help, always walk on the same side of the highway that your vehicle is on. You don't want to try crossing lanes when traffic is moving at high speeds.

➤ If your vehicle is disabled in a driving lane on the highway, activate the hazard flasher. Quickly put the hood in an up position. Safely get you and all passengers to the side of the road. Never stand directly behind or in front of your vehicle. Many collisions have occurred where occupants remained inside the vehicle or people have been hit while standing in the middle of the highway. If the situation warrants it, return to your vehicle and place reflectors at the rear of your vehicle.

Turn the pages to discover how to troubleshoot your vehicle and what to do when some unexpected driving situations occur.

Using Your Senses

Sights	
Symptoms	**Possible Causes**
Antifreeze underneath dashboard	• Faulty heater core • Cracked heater hose or valve
Black or blue smoke coming from tailpipe	• Dirty air filter • Incorrect air-fuel mixture • Low automatic transmission fluid • Incorrect grade of engine oil • Leaking exhaust manifold • Clogged fuel filter • Worn-out pistons
Brake fluid leaking	• Cracked brake hose • Leaking brake master cylinder • Leaking power brake booster • Leaking wheel cylinder(s)
Brown (or orange) automatic transmission fluid	• Damaged automatic transmission
Bubbles in antifreeze when engine is running	• Old antifreeze • Internal engine block leak
Carbon build-up on spark plug(s)	• Incorrect air-fuel mixture • Water in pistons • Incorrect type of spark plug(s) • Loose spark plug(s)

Sights (cont'd)	
Symptoms	**Possible Causes**
Corrosion in and around brake master cylinder	• Internal leak in master cylinder
Dark fluid around shock absorber(s)	• Defective shock absorber(s)
Dim headlights	• Worn-out alternator • Loose alternator belt • Discharged battery
Fire under hood	• Faulty electrical connections • Overabundance of gas in and around engine

Fluid spills underneath vehicle	1. Clear water near radiator (if vehicle is equipped with air conditioning)
	  ➤ Condensation from using the air conditioner. This is normal.
	  ➤ If there is no water underneath vehicle, air conditioning unit may be defective.
	
	2. Brown or black fluid
	  ➤ Engine oil
	
	3. Green fluid
	  ➤ Antifreeze
	
	4. Light tan fluid
	  ➤ Brake fluid, gas, or power steering fluid

Sights (cont'd)	
Symptoms	**Possible Causes**
	5. Reddish brown fluid ➤ Automatic transmission fluid or power steering fluid
Blown fuse	• Faulty circuit connection • Dirty wire connection • Worn-out wire insulation
Frothy engine oil	• Internal engine block leak • Too much oil in oil pan
Grey smoke coming from tailpipe	• Malfunctioning automatic transmission
Milky color on oil dipstick	• Internal antifreeze leak • Faulty head gasket
Milky color in power steering fluid	• Air locked in power steering system
Oil in coolant reservoir or radiator	• Leaking automatic transmission fluid • Internal engine block leak
Oil on spark plug(s)	• Faulty piston rings • Worn-out head gasket
Oil on oil dipstick	• Clean oil is honey-coloured • Old oil is brown or black • Reddish oil means automatic transmission fluid is seeping inside

Sights (cont'd)	
Symptoms	**Possible Causes**
Orange antifreeze	• Rusting radiator core
Vehicle sags to one side	• Defective shock absorber(s) strut(s) • Broken or worn-out springs
Steam coming from under hood	• See Troubleshooting: Overheating
Steering wheel off-centre	• Wheels out of alignment
Tan fluid around brake or clutch pedal	• Leaking brake master cylinder • Leaking clutch master cylinder
Water bubbles on automatic transmission fluid dipstick	• Old automatic transmission fluid
Water bubbles on oil dipstick	• Internal engine block leak • Very dirty engine oil
Water dripping from under dashboard	• Loose or cracked air conditioning hose • Leaking around outside rim along front windshield
Wet spark plug(s)	• Leaking brake fluid • Malfunctioning fuel-injection system (or carburetor), especially if spark plug(s) also smells of gas • Worn-out piston rings • Leaking transmission fluid

Sights (cont'd)	
Symptoms	**Possible Causes**
White smoke coming from tailpipe	• Antifreeze leak • Leaking head gasket
White smoke coming from tailpipe when engine is running	• Low antifreeze • Cracked cylinder head
White smoke around coolant system when engine is running	• Antifreeze leak
White stains around radiator	• Antifreeze leak
Windows do not defrost	• Defective heater core • Defective heater switch • Clogged ventilation outlets • Loose wire
Interior windows fog up	• Defective heater core
Windshield-washer fluid leaking inside trunk	• Parking on a steep incline for a long time (gravity forces washer fluid from rear window washer line into trunk)
Windshield wipers do not move	• Burned-out fuse • Defective windshield-wiper motor • Defective windshield-wiper switch • Loose wire

Smells	
Symptoms	**Possible Causes**
Burning oil when engine starts, but then dissipates	• Low automatic transmission fluid • Leaking engine block, such as cylinder head • Leaking oil around exhaust manifold (evident also by blue smoke coming from exhaust system)
Burning paint	• Malfunctioning cooling system (for example, radiator, thermostat, or water pump)
Burning plastic from under hood	• Wire short-circuiting • Burning wire insulation
Burning rubber from around tires	• Rubbing together of brake pads or shoes
Burning rubber from under hood	• Loose hose fallen on hot engine part • Wire insulation rubbing against hot engine part
Burnt smell on automatic transmission dipstick	• Damaged automatic transmission • Low or dirty automatic transmission fluid
Exhaust fumes	• Faulty exhaust pipe (carbon monoxide can seep into vehicle interior)

Smells (cont'd)	
Symptoms	**Possible Causes**
Gas smell	• Flooded carburetor • Faulty fuel-injection system • Leaking fuel line • Leaking fuel pump • Leaking fuel tank • Gas cap left open
Musty smell	• Plugged air conditioning unit • Water leaking into vehicle interior and staining carpets • Water seeping into trunk
Oil smell	• From a passing diesel vehicle • From oil refinery in area
Oil smell from under hood	• Clogged emission control system(s) • Low or no engine oil • Incorrect engine oil grade

Smells (cont'd)	
Symptoms	**Possible Causes**
Rotten egg smell	• Dirty air filter • Incorrect air-gas mixture • Damaged catalytic converter • Fuel fungus (in diesel vehicles)
Scorching odour underneath vehicle	• Overheating catalytic converter
Smoke smell in interior of vehicle	• Burning cigarette butt on the seat
Sour milk smell	• Spilled milk on carpet or seat (or inside trunk) that has been sitting awhile
Sweet Smell	• Antifreeze leak • Discharging battery

YOU WONDER WHY A PLUGGED CATALYTIC
CONVERTER SMELLS LIKE ROTTEN EGGS......UGH!!
WHY NOT LIKE ROSES?

Sounds	
Symptoms	**Possible Causes**
Vehicle backfires	• Incorrect air-fuel mixture • Low automatic transmission fluid • Damp or cracked distributor cap • Clogged fuel filter • Dirty or incorrectly gapped spark plug(s)
Buzzing when windshield wipers are on	• Empty windshield-washer reservoir
Clicking from radio	• Incorrectly gapped spark plug(s) • Loose spark plug wire(s)
Clicking when trying to start engine	• Worn-out alternator • Loose alternator belt • Discharged battery • Corroded or frayed battery cables • Cracked or old distributor cap • Low engine oil • Incorrect grade of engine oil • Dirty spark plug(s) wires • Faulty starter • Loose wire between ignition switch and starter

Sounds (cont'd)	
Symptoms	**Possible Causes**
Clicking from a front wheel when turning a corner	• Cracked boot covering on CV-joint • Worn-out strut mount assembly
Clunk underneath vehicle when shifting gears	• Slipping automatic transmission gears • Loose CV-joint • Low or dirty transmission fluid • Defective U-joint
Grinding around wheels	• A normal sound if heard only when the brakes are applied • If noise heard constantly, the disc-brake wear indicator is letting you know brake pads are worn thin • Worn-out or dry wheel bearings
Hissing from around radiator	• Faulty radiator cap • Small leak in radiator core
Howling from rear of vehicle	• Worn-out rear differential • Low rear differential fluid
Knocking (pinging) under hood	• Broken belt (for example, timing) • Low engine oil • Incorrect grade of engine oil • Stuck emission control system(s) • Bad gas • Incorrect gas type • Faulty pistons • Incorrectly gapped spark plug(s)

Sounds (cont'd)	
Symptoms	**Possible Causes**
No sound when ignition key is turned to "on"	• Faulty alternator • Discharged or dead battery • Loose battery cables • Blown fuse or fusible link • Defective ignition switch or wire • Safety belt not engaged • Faulty starter or starter solenoid • Transmission not in "P" (automatic) or "L" or "N" (manual)
Rattling from around tire	• Incorrectly installed brake pads • Worn-out or missing brake parts • Stone, pebble, or other object lodged between hubcap and tire
Rattling from front or back of vehicle	• Loose hood latch • Loose licence plate • Loose trunk latch
Rattling from underneath vehicle	• Deteriorating exhaust parts (for example, muffler or tailpipe) • Loose or broken hangers and clamps along exhaust system
Rumbling (or spitting) from rear of vehicle	• Exhaust leak (carbon monoxide fumes may be entering vehicle's interior)
Singing from under hood	• Loose or frayed belt (such as fan belt) • Faulty radiator cap

Sounds (cont'd)	
Symptoms	**Possible Causes**
Snapping from under hood	• Loose or shorting-out spark plug wire(s)
Squeaking when air conditioner turned on	• A normal sound if air conditioner has not been used for awhile and should stop once unit operates for a few minutes
Squealing from under hood	• Bent air-cleaner cover • Faulty alternator • Loose or worn-out belt (such as fan belt or belt on power steering pump) • Low fluid in power steering pump • Faulty water pump
Thumping from tire	• Incorrect air pressure in one tire • Improper wheel balance • Flat spots on tire • Improper wheel alignment
Thumping from underneath vehicle when gas or brake pedal is applied	• Worn-out ball joints • Defective shock absorber(s) strut(s) • Worn-out U-joint
Thunk when driving across bumps, holes, or railway crossings	• Worn-out shock absorber(s) strut(s) • Broken or worn-out springs

Sounds (cont'd)	
Symptoms	**Possible Causes**
Ticking under hood when vehicle is idling	• Low engine oil • Faulty valve in engine block
Whining under hood when starting engine, but not when engine is idling	• Low transmission fluid
Whirring when trying to start vehicle	• Faulty driveshaft • Defective starter
Whistling of air when vehicle is idling or in motion	• Clogged air filter • Loose fan belt • Broken or disconnected hose • Malfunctioning positive crankcase ventilation (PCV) valve • Stuck throttle linkage at the carburetor

Feel of Vehicle	
Symptoms	**Possible Causes**
Bounces after driving over bumps or holes	• Defective shock absorber(s) (struts)
Does not move when gas pedal is applied	• Stuck brake pads (from being wet) • Objects at tires (such as rocks or toys) • Low or dirty automatic transmission fluid • Low or no fluid in clutch master cylinder (manual transmission)

I THINK I NEED A
GOOD CHECK-UP

Feel of Vehicle (cont'd)

Symptoms	Possible Causes
Idles roughly	• Dirty air filter • Low automatic transmission fluid • Worn-out belt (for example, timing belt) • Clutch linkage out of adjustment • Worn-out C- or U-joints • Damp distributor cap • Stuck or clogged emission control system(s) • Bent or clogged muffler or tailpipe • Plugged fuel filter • Dirty fuel injectors • Dirt or water in fuel tank • Bad gas • Leaking or kinked hose • Improperly gapped or dirty spark plug(s) • Frayed spark plug wire(s), or they are not secured to spark plug(s) or top of distributor cap

| **Feel of Vehicle (cont'd)** ||
Symptoms	**Possible Causes**
Loses power when accelerating	• Discharging battery • Dirty battery cables • Plugged or defective catalytic converter • Faulty charging system (for example, dirty or corroded battery cables) • Faulty computer system • Plugged fuel filter • Blocked or leaking fuel line • Defective fuel pump • Low gas in fuel tank • Leaking head gasket • Worn-out pistons
Moves while parking brake engaged	• Loose or broken parking brake cable

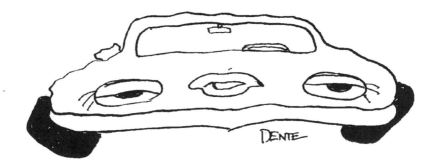

GOSH, IT MUST BE TIME FOR A TUNE-UP.
I....FEEL....SO.... SLUGGISH........

Feel of Vehicle (cont'd)

Symptoms	Possible Causes
No power when accelerating	• Plugged catalytic converter • Slipping clutch (manual transmission) • Faulty distributor • Damp or cracked distributor cap • Stuck or clogged emission control system(s) • Plugged fuel filter • Faulty fuel pump • Dirt or water in fuel tank • Bent or clogged muffler or tailpipe • Broken or disconnected clutch-pedal return spring • Defective sensor in computer system • Incorrectly gapped or dirty spark plug(s) • Frayed spark plug wire(s) or not fully connected to spark plug(s)
Pulls right or left after going through deep water	• Water in braking system

Feel of Vehicle (cont'd)	
Symptoms	**Possible Causes**
Pulls to one side when accelerating	• Worn-out ball joints • Flat front tire on side vehicle pulls towards • Engaged parking brake • Loose or defective rack-and-pinion steering unit • Defective shock absorber(s) (struts) • Broken or sagging springs • Uneven tire pressure or tire tread on one front tire • Different-sized tires on vehicle • Wheels out of alignment
Pulls to one side when braking	• Incorrect air pressure on one tire • Wet brakes • Loose or stuck caliper(s) • Worn-out brake hoses or lines • Dirt in brake system (for example, hoses, lines, or master cylinder) • Defective shock absorber(s) (struts) • Improper wheel alignment
Stalls in cold weather	• Dirty air filter • Discharging battery • Defective coolant temperature sensor • Dirty fuel injectors (or carburetor) • Clogged fuel filter • Defective fuel pump • Faulty spark plug(s)

Feel of Vehicle (cont'd)

Symptoms	Possible Causes
Stalls in hot weather	• See Troubleshooting: Overheating
Stalls when engine is idling	• Dirty air filter • Low automatic transmission fluid • Clogged fuel filter • Bad or little gas in fuel tank • Faulty spark plug(s) • Defective thermostat
Steering difficulties	• Worn-out ball joints • Loose or broken belt on power steering pump • Damaged front-end suspension parts (for example, ball joints) • Loose, broken, or kinked hose connected to steering pump • Worn-out rack-and-pinion steering unit • Dry and cracked rubber seals at ends of rack-and-pinion steering unit • Low power steering fluid • Defective power steering pump • Flat tire at front or rear • Low or uneven tire pressure • Front wheels out of alignment

Feel of Vehicle (cont'd)	
Symptoms	**Possible Causes**
Trouble starting	• Dirty air filter • Loose alternator belt • Discharging battery • Loose or dirty battery cables or terminals • Faulty computer system (for example, sensors) • Cracked or damp distributor cap • Clogged fuel filter • Clogged fuel injectors (or carburetor) • Defective fuel pump • Bad gas • No gas in fuel tank • Faulty ignition switch • Dirty or improperly gapped spark plug(s) • Wet spark plug(s) wires • Defective starter

Feel of Vehicle (cont'd)	
Symptoms	**Possible Causes**
Vibrates (shakes) when moving	• Air locked inside brake system • Defective CV- or U-joint • Defective fuel injectors (or carburetor) • Defective disc or drum brakes • Worn-out driveshaft • Loose exhaust pipe • Incorrect tire pressure on front tire • Unbalanced front tires (shaking is noticeable at highway speeds; if vibration is intermittent, rear tires are unbalanced) • Lead weight (used for tire balancing) on one tire has fallen off • Loose lug nuts at wheels • Defective shock absorber(s) (struts) • Incorrectly gapped spark plug(s) • Bent tire rim • Worn-out steering linkage
Weaves back and forth	• Flat rear tire • Worn-out suspension parts (such as ball joints or springs) • Wheels out of alignment

Other Mechanical Deficiencies

Air Conditioner

For safety reasons, a professional mechanic should service all parts of the air conditioner (the refrigerant is very explosive).

Deficiency	Possible Causes
Malfunctioning air conditioning unit	• Loose or broken belt around compressor • Burned-out blower motor • Defective compressor • Debris on condenser • Burned-out fuse • Cracked air conditioner hose • Low refrigerant

Automatic Transmission

Deficiency	Possible Causes
Vehicle wants to move forward or back when it is in "D" or "R" and one foot is on the brake and the other foot gently accelerates the gas pedal	• Slipping transmission gears
Automatic transmission fluid smells burnt and/or fluid feels gritty	• Defective bands, filter, fluid, gasket, or plates inside the transmission
Automatic transmission fluid leaks	• Leaking transmission filter located inside transmission pan • Worn-out gasket • Leaking front seal in transmission

Automatic Transmission (cont'd)	
Deficiency	**Possible Causes**
Transmission damage	• Putting gear in "D" or "R" and driving without letting engine warm up transmission fluid

Brake Pedal	
Deficiency	**Possible Causes**
Hard to push	• Overheated brakes • Wet brakes • Cracked or kinked brake hose • Leaking brake lines • Faulty brake master cylinder • Glazed brake pads or shoes
Moves slowly to floor when foot stops depressing pedal	• Low brake fluid • Defective brake master cylinder • Worn-out brake pads or shoes • Air locked inside brake system
Feels soft or spongy	• Faulty caliper(s) • Low or contaminated brake fluid • Cracked brake hose • Worn-out brake lines • Loose brake-pedal linkage • Air locked inside brake system
Sticks when applying brakes	• Worn-out brake hose • Stuck brake-pedal linkage

Brake Pedal (cont'd)	
Deficiency	**Possible Causes**
Vibrates	• Antilock brake system (ABS) is activated (vibration is normal) • Air locked inside brake system • Warped calipers or rotors (disc brakes) • Defective drums (drum brakes) • Cracked brake hoses
Squeaks	• Improperly installed brakes • Clogged brake lines • Defective brake parts (such as drum, pads, plates, or springs) • Disc-brake wear indicator indicating brake pads are thin • Sometimes disc brakes squeak or vibrate "just because" that is the way metallic brake pads and disc rotors are built (squeaking or vibrating is a normal sound)
Pressure applied and interior dome light goes on	• Blown fuse

Gauges

Deficiency	Possible Causes
Gauges on instrument panel do not work	• Defective alternator • Blown fuse • Loose or corroded wiring

Indicator Lights on the Dashboard

If an indicator light turns red while driving, use as little of the accessories as possible. This is especially important if the battery charge light stays on. Stop your vehicle as soon as safely possible to avoid engine failure.

Deficiency	Possible Causes
Light stays red after engine is started or a light turns red while driving	• Malfunctioning computer system • Serious engine problems relating to specific light • Burned-out fuse • Loose wire under the dashboard
Air bag light stays on	• Faulty air bag • Short circuit in the computer system
Antilock brake (ABS) light stays on	• Activated ABS (normal for light to go on) • Malfunctioning ABS (conventional brakes are working, but only if brake light stays off) • Sticking brake calipers • Low brake fluid in brake master cylinder

Indicator Lights on the Dashboard (cont'd)	
Deficiency	**Possible Causes**
Battery (charge) light stays on	• Faulty alternator • Dead or discharged battery • Electrical current malfunction running to or from the battery • Loose fan belt
Brake light stays on	• Burned-out bulb (if there is no brake light on only one side of vehicle) • Defective brake-failure warning switch (if there are no lights on both sides of vehicle) • Low or contaminated brake fluid • Air locked inside brake line • Sticking disc-brake caliper(s) • Leaking brake hoses or lines • Faulty brake master cylinder • Defective parking brake • Deteriorated rear brake shoes
Emissions light stays on	• Defective or clogged emission control device (such as exhaust gas recirculation [EGR])
Engine light stays on	• Defective alternator • Discharging battery • Faulty emissions system • Loose or broken fan belt • Clogged or leaking fuel line

Indicator Lights on the Dashboard (cont'd)

Deficiency	Possible Causes
Engine oil light stays on	• Low engine oil • Incorrect grade of engine oil • Internal oil leak in engine block • Defective oil pump
Parking brake warning light stays on	• Burned-out bulb • Low brake fluid • Parking brake not fully released • Frozen or broken parking brake cable
Temperature light stays on	• Overheating (see Troubleshooting: Overheating)
Seat belt reminder light stays on	• Lap and shoulder belts not fully engaged

Lights

Deficiency	Possible Causes
Back-up Lights White light does not go on when vehicle put in reverse	• Defective back-up light switch • Burned-out bulb • Loose wiring
Brake Lights Red light does not go on one side when brake pedal is depressed	• Burned-out bulb
Red light on either side does not go on	• Defective switch at brake pedal

Lights (cont'd)	
Deficiency	**Possible Causes**
Headlights One headlight works on high beam, but not on low beam	• Burned-out bulb at headlight
Headlights do not work on either low or high beam	• Blown or "open" fuse, fusible link, or circuit breaker • Loose, dirty, or severed wire connection
Headlight looks "dark" when not turned on	• Insides of headlight is burning out (headlight must be replaced, rather than just the bulb)
Signal Lights Only one front or rear signal light blinks on and off, or one bulb flashes faster	• Burned-out bulb
One or all signal lights flicker on and off	• Dirty bulb socket • Loose wire around socket
All four signal lights (two in front and two in rear) do not blink	• Faulty flasher (relay) bulb
Signal lights do not disengage	• Defective signal switch

Lights (cont'd)

Deficiency	Possible Causes
One green arrow signal light (on dashboard) goes on but does not blink; does not make ticking sound; or blinks slower or faster than normal	• Burned-out signal bulb at front or rear of vehicle
Both green arrow signal lights (on dashboard) go on but do not blink	• Burned-out flasher bulb

Overheating the Radiator and Cooling System

Deficiency	Possible Causes
Antifreeze leaks	• Corroded freeze-out plugs • Leaking gasket at thermostat or engine • Loose petcock (drain) plug • Faulty radiator cap • Worn-out (thin) radiator core • Leaking radiator hoses • Faulty water pump
Loose fan	• Faulty water pump

Overheating the Radiator and Cooling System (cont'd)

Deficiency	Possible Causes
Two heater hoses do not "feel" the same temperature	• Stuck heater control valve • Clogged heater core • Clogged or kinked heater hose • Air has entered heating system • Defective heater and defroster motor • Clogged radiator • Faulty thermostat
Overheating	• Low antifreeze • Frozen antifreeze (result of inadequate antifreeze-water mixture) • Defective antifreeze recovery tank • Loose or broken belts (such as fan belt) • Clogged catalytic converter • Cracked cylinder head • Clogged or cracked freeze-out plugs • Vapour lock (air bubbles) in fuel line • Leaking head gasket at engine block • Faulty heater core • Clogged muffler or tailpipe • Faulty radiator cap • Defective radiator core • Debris on outside of radiator core • Clogged or cracked upper or lower radiator hose • Defective thermostat • Faulty water pump

Overheating the Radiator and Cooling System (cont'd)

Deficiency	Possible Causes
No antifreeze moving through radiator or radiator hoses	• Clogged radiator hose • Faulty thermostat • Faulty water pump
Soft radiator hoses when engine is cold, but expand when radiator cap is removed	• Faulty radiator cap
Collapsed lower radiator hose	• Defective water pump
Temperature gauge on dashboard rises slowly	• Stuck (open) thermostat
Temperature gauge on dashboard rises quickly to red zone	• Stuck (closed) thermostat

*NOW I'M REALLY STEAMED. I KNEW THAT
RAD OF A HOSE NEEDED CHANGING!*

Tires	
Deficiency	**Possible Causes**
Poor gas mileage, difficulty in steering	• Underinflated tires
Reduced traction, especially on ice and wet surfaces	• Overinflated tires
Improper wheel alignment	• Underinflated tires • Uneven tire tread • Driving over curbs, bumps, or potholes
Both outside edges of tire treads worn down	• Underinflated tires
Centre of tire tread worn down	• Overinflated tires
Uneven tread wear across the entire tire	• Defective ball joints or shock absorber(s)

Scenarios – What to Do

Scenario	What To Do
Fire from a tire	• Put out the fire using a fire extinguisher, by throwing dirt on it, or by applying a steady stream of water until the tire is cool enough to handle.
	• If the heat is coming from inside the tire, the fire will be difficult to extinguish. Stay away from the tire and seek help.
Fire under the hood	• Safely stop your vehicle at the roadside.
	• Immediately turn the ignition key to "off."
	• Release the inside hood latch.
	• Immediately leave your vehicle.
	• Use a fire extinguisher, baking soda, dirt, or sand to extinguish the fire only if it is safe to attempt. Never use water to douse the fire. Water added to burning electrical parts enhances flames.
	• For safety reasons, your best course of action is to leave the hood closed (release the inside hood latch) and let firefighters put out the fire. Maintain a safe distance from your vehicle until help arrives.

Sceniarios - What To Do (cont'd)

Scenario	What To Do
Flooded engine	• It is often necessary to wait five to ten minutes before restarting the engine. • On fuel-injected vehicles, hold the gas pedal a quarter to halfway to the floor for about 15 seconds, or depress the pedal all the way to the floor for about 30 seconds. Although a flooded engine in a fuel-injected vehicle can happen in cold temperatures, you should not be experiencing a flooded engine in the spring, summer, or fall. • On vehicles with carburetors, depress the gas pedal halfway to the floor or hold it all the way to the floor until your vehicle starts. Be careful not to damage the starter from the constant revving of the engine.
Fuel line vapour lock	• Place a clean wet cloth on the fuel line or wrap tin foil around it. • Drive to the nearest service centre.
Hood pops up while driving	• Do not slam on the brakes. • Slowly reduce vehicle speed. • For visibility, carefully look between the dashboard and hood or roll down the driver's window. • Activate the hazard flasher. • Signal and safely drive to the roadside. • Tie the hood down with a rope.

Sceniarios - What To Do (cont'd)

Scenario	What To Do
Vehicle gets stuck	• Turn off all electrical accessories and roll down the window to hear the tires spinning.
	• Removing some air from the tires may help to dislodge your vehicle. Keep the front wheels pointed straight.
	• Put something for traction under the tires, such as kitty litter or old carpets.
	• Never have a person stand in front of or directly behind your vehicle.
	• You can try to "rock" your vehicle free. For an automatic transmission, repeatedly shift from "D" or the next lower gear to "R" and back again, braking quickly between shifts. On a manual transmission, shift from "2" to "R." Use caution when abruptly shifting gears as this may cause transmission failure.
	• If the tires and engine get hot, let everything cool down before starting the above procedure again.
Vehicle skids	• Do not immediately apply the brakes.
	• Ease up on the accelerator.
	• Keep your eyes focused on where you want to go, rather than looking directly in front of your vehicle.
	• With both hands on the steering wheel, turn in the direction you want the front of your vehicle to head towards. Once your vehicle returns to a straight line, keep the steering wheel centred, but watch for skidding in the opposite direction. Often, it takes more than one steering wheel turn to get out of a skid.

...cont'd

| Sceniarios - What To Do (cont'd) ||
Scenario	**What To Do**
Vehicle skids (cont'd)	• Try to move your vehicle towards an open space. • On an automatic transmission vehicle, do not shift into "N" (some experts state that, by putting the transmission into neutral, vehicle control improves). On a manual transmission vehicle, gently apply pressure to the brake pedal and quickly depress the clutch pedal, to take away power from the drive wheels.
Vehicle drives off the paved road	• Never swerve your vehicle back onto the paved road. • Keep a firm grip on the steering wheel. • Ease up on the gas pedal. • Gently apply pressure to the brake pedal to maintain control of your vehicle. • Signal, shoulder check, and then ease your vehicle back onto the road.

YIKES! SLIPPERY!!
STAY COOL, GIRL....
STAY COOL

Battery

Pre-Boosting Checklist

✔ Trust your instincts with the person offering to boost your discharged battery. If you don't feel comfortable with the individual, firmly decline the offer.

✔ Vehicles with a computerized (electronic) system can cause a surge when the booster cables are hooked up or removed. Some automotive manufacturers do not recommend boosting another vehicle so consult both vehicle owner manuals. A decal may also be affixed under the hood that advises not to boost.

✔ Remove jewellery and anything else from your hands and wrists before boosting.

✔ Boost only between one 12-volt battery and another 12-volt battery (each battery has six vent caps). Or, boost between a 6-volt battery and another 6-volt battery (each battery has three vent caps). Never boost a 12-volt with a 6-volt battery.

✔ The battery in a diesel vehicle has a higher electrical power than most conventional automobiles. Do not boost a diesel if your vehicle is not a diesel and vice versa.

✔ Never boost a vehicle if the electrolyte inside the battery is frozen, which often happens in cold weather.

✔ Never boost a battery if the indicator shows no colour as this usually means the electrolyte level is low. Gases are probably seeping and the battery could explode if booster cables are hooked to its posts.

✔ Before boosting, make sure no accessories are on in the live and the discharged vehicles. For example, close all doors so that the interior light is not on.

✔ The bodies of the two vehicles should never touch each other when boosting.

✔ Booster cables are colour coded: red is positive (+) and black is negative (–).

✔ Negative booster cables are not effective when hooked to a painted surface. Hook the negative cable to a metal part under the hood.

✔ The booster cables should not have loose, missing, or exposed wires.

✔ The length and gauge of booster cables can affect success in charging the discharged battery. Ideally, use a 5 m (16 ft.), 16-gauge booster cable with sturdy clamps.

✔ Never touch battery clamps together, especially when one end is attached to the battery as sparks can result or the battery explode.

✔ Once the discharged vehicle has been boosted, let the engine run for approximately five minutes before driving. This gives sufficient time to recharge the battery and avoid surging the interior accessories, such as the clock.

MAYBE IF I ACT REAL COY, A GOOD LOOKING 12 VOLT WILL COME ALONG

Boosting Procedure

Caution is advised when boosting any vehicle. Read the preceding pre-boosting checklist before starting the boosting procedure.

1. Set the transmission to "P" (automatic) or "N" (manual).

2. Apply the parking brake to each vehicle.

3. Turn the ignition keys in each vehicle to the "off" position.

4. If possible, remove the vent caps from each battery.

5. Hook the positive (+) booster cable (red) to the positive (+) battery post on the discharged vehicle.

6. Hook the other positive (+) booster cable to the positive (+) battery post on the live vehicle.

7. Hook the negative (–) booster cable (black) to the negative (–) battery post on the live vehicle.

8. Hook the other negative (–) booster cable to an unpainted metal part on the discharged vehicle. Do not attach the cable to the negative (–) battery post on the discharged vehicle. Place the clamp on the negative cable as far from the battery as possible.

9. Leave the connected vehicles alone for a couple of minutes to let the electrical current start flowing into the discharged battery. This is especially important if the discharged battery is cold.

10. Turn the ignition key to "on" in the discharged vehicle. You should not have to turn the ignition on in the live vehicle because there should be sufficient juice flowing from the charged battery to the discharged battery.

11. Remove the negative (–) booster cable from the now charging vehicle and then disconnect the negative (–) booster cable from the live vehicle.

12. Remove the positive (+) booster cable from the live vehicle and then disconnect the positive (+) booster cable from the now charging vehicle.

13. Replace the vent caps on each battery.

14. Ideally, let the engine run for 10 to 15 minutes, to recharge the battery, before turning the ignition off.

Flat Tire

Steps to take when driving and your vehicle gets a flat tire

- Firmly hold the steering wheel (lots of vibration occurs).
- Keep your vehicle moving in a straight line.
- Do not suddenly apply your foot to the brake pedal.
- Slowly take your right foot off the gas pedal.
- Once your vehicle is under control, gently apply pressure to the brake pedal.
- Never abruptly turn the steering wheel right or left.
- Signal, then safely park on the roadside, preferably on level ground. Never park on a bridge, overpass, or a curved road.

GRIP THAT STEERING
WHEEL GIRL, WE'RE
COMING IN
FOR A LANDING

Personal safety precautions when changing a flat tire

- If someone stops to offer assistance, trust your instincts. It may be in your best interest to have that person phone for roadside assistance. Never get inside a vehicle with a stranger.

- It should take only 10 to 15 minutes to change a flat tire.

- Make sure the spare has enough air pressure before starting to remove the flat tire.

- Ideally, have your vehicle on level ground when changing a flat tire.

- Turn the ignition key to "off," set the gear set to "P" (automatic) or "L" (manual), and engage the parking brake.

- Put the hazard flasher on and open the hood. If the temperature is well below zero, leave the hood closed or the engine will freeze.

- Use a well-constructed jack and know where the reinforced areas (notches) are on your vehicle. The specific locations are outlined on the jack stand or in your vehicle owner's manual.

- Place a piece of plywood underneath the jack stand to secure it.

- Use gloves to remove the blown-out tire (the tire can be very hot).

- Take your time. Rushing can cause personal injury.

- When changing a flat tire facing oncoming traffic, be extra cautious you do not unconsciously step onto the highway. If travelling with a passenger, have that person constantly watch out for your safety.

Safety precautions for others when changing a flat tire

- Park your vehicle off to the side of the road as much as possible, so as not to obstruct traffic.

- If you are on the shoulder of a highway, engage the hazard flasher and use reflectors. Place two to three reflectors starting about ten vehicle lengths behind your vehicle. Set the reflectors 5 m (16 ft.) apart. Or tie a cloth to one door handle closest to traffic. For increased visibility, put the hood up and leave the trunk open.

- All vehicle occupants should remain in a safe location outside your vehicle.

Procedure for changing a flat tire

1. Remove the spare tire and all other necessary tools from the trunk and place them on the ground beside the flat tire.

2. Secure the remaining tires using pieces of wood or rocks.

3. Safely set the jack and jack stand in an appropriate position, near to the side of the flat tire. Do not jack up the vehicle.

4. Remove the hubcap using a flathead screwdriver.

5. Place the hubcap near you. That way, the lugs (nuts) can be placed inside the cap once removed from the wheel.

6. Using a lug wrench and a pipe for leverage, loosen the wheel lugs counterclockwise. Loosen the lugs in a crisscross manner, but do not fully remove them from the threaded studs (bolts). The lugs should be loose enough to be removed by hand once your vehicle has been jacked.

7. Place the piece of wood under the jack stand. Using solid, even strokes on the jack, raise your vehicle enough so that the flat tire is off the road and can freely move around.

8. Once the jack is raised, wiggle it and the stand to make sure they are secure on the ground and to your vehicle. Put pressure on your vehicle to check that it can't move.

9. Safely walk around your vehicle and doublecheck the wood or rocks. They should be firmly secured against the tires.

10. Remove the wheel lugs by hand in a crisscross pattern and place them in the hubcap.

11. Safely sit in front of or kneel at the flat tire. Put on gloves and wiggle the tire loose from the bolts using both hands.

12. Roll the flat tire to the rear of your vehicle, laying it beside the trunk.

13. Position the spare tire beside the wheel. In a sitting or kneeling position, place the spare tire onto the bolts.

14. Replace the wheel lugs, hand tightening in a crisscross pattern.

15. Tighten the wheel lugs with the lug wrench in a crisscross pattern.

16. Lower the jack so that your vehicle has all its tires on the pavement. Safely remove the jack stand.

17. Tighten the wheel lugs in a crisscross pattern using the lug wrench.

18. Sit or kneel in front of the tire to replace the hubcap, tapping lightly all around all it using a rag-covered hammer.

19. Remove the wood or blocks from around the tires, set the flat tire inside the trunk along with the tools and supplies.

Sudden Stops

Vehicle has antilock brakes
- Maintain a steady grip on the steering wheel.
- Remove your right foot from the gas pedal.
- "Heel and toe" the brake pedal – keep your right foot on the floor and use your toes on the brake pedal.
- Apply firm and steady pressure to the brake pedal. Never pump the brakes.

Vehicle does not have antilock brakes
- Maintain a steady grip on the steering wheel.
- Remove your right foot from the gas pedal.
- "Heel and toe" the brake pedal - keep your right foot on the floor and use your toes on the brake pedal.
- Apply a steady, pumping action to the brake pedal (put pressure on the pedal, ease up, put pressure on the pedal, ease up, and so on).

Brakes Fail

Vehicle has anti-lock brakes

- Maintain a firm grip on the steering wheel with both hands.
- Gently apply pressure to the brake pedal. If the antilock braking system isn't working, the conventional brakes should still be functioning.
- Never pump the brake pedal.
- If the conventional brakes fail, slowly pump the parking brake.

Vehicle does not have anti-lock brakes

- Maintain a firm grip on the steering wheel with both hands.
- Rapidly pump the brakes.
- If pumping the brakes does not work, slowly pump the parking brake.
- If the parking brake does not work:
  - ➤ Automatic transmission vehicle: move the gear from "D" to "2," then to "1," and back to "D."
  - ➤ Manual transmission vehicle: put the gearshift into a lower gear and slowly release the clutch.

Deep Water

Vehicle drives through deep water

- By lightly applying the brakes, water from inside the brakes has an opportunity to drain out.

Vehicle submerges in deep water

- Once your vehicle is in water, release your seat belt. Do not release it before, as you want to be secured in your seat upon impact.
- Quickly lower your window.
- If the window sticks, open the door. Stay calm, the door will open as the water rises.
- It takes three to five minutes for a vehicle to completely sink.

OH, OH, ! GOTTA KEEP THE
WATER OUT OF MY IMPORTANT PARTS

Overheating Engine

Driving in heavy stop-and-go traffic

- Turn off the air conditioner.

- Open all windows.

- Turn on the heater and fan to their highest settings.

- When temporarily stopped, shift into "N" and slowly rev the engine.

- Do not "ride the brakes" when your vehicle is moving.

- Maintain some distance from the vehicle ahead to avoid hot exhaust fumes adding heat to your vehicle's already hot engine.

- Safely move your vehicle to the roadside.

Once ignition key is turned to "off"

- Overheating can destroy the engine block and other parts, such as the transmission, which is why it is important not to operate your vehicle when it is overheating.

- The engine must be cool before anything can be done.

- Never open the hood if steam is coming from underneath it.

- Once the steam has subsided, slowly open the hood.

- If the radiator cap has a pressure-release device, open the lever using a screwdriver, not your hand. Wait for the hissing from the pressure release radiator cap to stop before completely removing the cap.

- Wearing a glove, remove the radiator cap at an angle, away from you, and in a counterclockwise motion.

- Start the engine.

- Slowly add water or antifreeze (antifreeze and water mixture) to the radiator.

Weather-Related Emergency Procedures

Distress Calls And Signals

- Use your cellular phone to dial 911. No long distance charges apply, which means you do not have to dial 0 or the area code before punching in 911. Pre-program 911 on your cellular phone. You can also dial *611 (or 611) and a customer service representative will redirect your call to the nearest 911 dispatch. Dialing 411 (directory assistance) will also get you put through to the appropriate operator.

- Dialing 911 should be used in an emergency only to inform the dispatcher of situations, such as a traffic accident, traffic hazard, drunk driver, medical emergency, fire, driver in distress, or crime in progress. Provide the dispatcher with specifics (for example, your exact location, including street names, direction of travel, distinguishing landmarks, etc.).

- A white cloth is a universal distress symbol, but a brightly coloured cloth also suffices.

- A SOS is completed in sets of threes - three dots (short signals), three dashes (long signals). You can use the following to send a distress signal:

  - Horn - three short beeps, three long beeps

  - Headlights or flashlight - three short flashes, three long flashes

  - Mirrors or other shiny object - three short flashes, three long flashes

In The Back Roads

- Place a "Help" or "Police" sign across the rear or front window (see *AutoTalk Assistant*).

- Tape reflector tape across the hood, roof, and trunk.

- Tie a white or brightly coloured cloth to the radio antenna or one of the door handles.

- Safely set a fire. Dark smoke can be achieved by burning rubber parts from your vehicle or adding engine oil to the fire. If possible, safely set three separate fires. Secure the fire with rocks and have water available. Never set the fire close to your vehicle.

- Disturb the area around you. Tie coloured rags to trees; cut bushes and trees.

- Never drink any of the fluids from under the hood; they are poisonous.

- If you decide to leave your vehicle, place a note on the dashboard (see *AutoTalk Assistant*). Leave the interior and exterior lights on in the vehicle, as you want it to be as bright as possible, even though you won't be in it. Make sure you are adequately dressed for changing weather conditions.

Caught In A Snowstorm

- In most cases, it is safer to stay inside your vehicle, rather than try to walk for help. It offers shelter as long as the following precautions are taken.

  ➤ Tie a brightly coloured cloth to the radio antenna or one of the door handles.

  ➤ Place a "Police" or "Help" sign across the rear or front window (see *AutoTalk Assistant*).

  ➤ Remove the emergency package from the trunk.

  ➤ Pad your vehicle with snow, including the underside. Make sure the area around the tailpipe is clear of snow so that carbon monoxide fumes don't seep into the interior of your vehicle.

I'LL BET YOU'VE NEVER SEEN THIS DONE BEFORE

- If your vehicle still has power, turn the engine on for ten minutes every hour to keep the battery charged.
- Leave interior vents and ducts open.
- Remove ice and snow from the exterior window grilles.
- Insulate the windows and any metal parts in the interior with carpets, newspapers, and rubber floor mats.
- Place a lighted candle (inside an empty tin cup) on the dashboard.
- Bundle yourself up in the front or back seat, not on the floor. Always wear a hat.
- Write notes, such as the time you stopped, the date, and your eating times. Putting pen to paper also helps keep you focused.
- To keep warm and stay awake, constantly change your position. Read, write, exercise, sing, or do whatever you need to do to *not* fall asleep.

Earthquake

- Immediately stop your vehicle, but not on an over- or underpass or a bridge as they could collapse.
- Stay inside your vehicle.

Lightning Storm

- Immediately stop your vehicle.
- Do not park under power lines or trees.
- Seek shelter. If there is none, stay inside your vehicle.
- Do not use any electrical accessories, such as the radio, even if the engine isn't running.
- Keep your feet on a rubber mat.

Tornado

- Immediately stop your vehicle.
- Leave your vehicle and seek shelter or lie flat on your stomach in a ditch or other low-lying area.
- Protect your head.

Collisions

Involved In A Collision With Another Vehicle

- In most cases, you should call the local police. Dial 911 if medical attention is required. Give the dispatcher specific information, such as number and extent of injuries, number of vehicles involved, exact location of collision, if a tow truck is required, number of traffic lanes blocked, whether gas has been spilled, and if you are a witness or someone involved in the collision.

- Turn off the engine in all vehicles involved. Only move the vehicles if they are obstructing other traffic; otherwise, leave everything as is.

- Do not smoke, especially if there is spilled fuel.

- Obtain first aid for the injured. The Emergency Medical Aid Act (Good Samaritan Act) applies here.

- Ensure everyone else is safely off the road.

- Look for victims thrown from a vehicle.

- Be cautious of your words as they could be used against you in a lawsuit.

- Use reflectors behind the collision to warn other motorists. Do not use flares; they can ignite if fuel has been spilled.

- See *AutoTalk Assistant* for a collision report.

Hitting An Unoccupied Vehicle

- See *AutoTalk Assistant* for a form to complete.

Hitting an Animal

- At night, animals freeze up in the bright headlights. To scare the animal from the road, flicker the headlights and blow the horn.

- If you hit an animal, whether it is someone's pet or a wild animal, contact the local police or SPCA.

Locked Inside The Trunk

- You have a number of options if you are locked inside the trunk of a vehicle:

    ➤ Locate the trunk release device (if you know the trunk has one).

    ➤ Find the cloth bag (see *Exterior of Your Vehicle*: "Emergency Package") and use its contents to open the trunk or make noises.

    ➤ Pull at the wires and bulbs close to the rear lights. Doing this will cause the brake lights to not work, which might alert a police cruiser driving behind you.

Section 6
Behind the Wheel

There are many things to consider before you get behind the wheel, such as your health and frame of mind. Once you start driving, other vehicle traffic, pedestrians and animals, and traffic-control devices vie for your attention. After your vehicle is parked, safety precautions are necessary (for example, close and lock all doors). There are also things to keep in mind when driving alone. Taking a vacation involves checklists to make sure you and your family are safe and comfortable inside your vehicle.

This section looks at all these aspects in an effort to make your time on the road enjoyable.

SECTION SIX CONTENTS

...cont'd

Introduction

Driving involves co-operation, trust, and human interaction, even though you are sometimes alone in your vehicle. While on the road, you must participate with other drivers, trusting both your own ability to drive and other motorists. And all this happening inside the confined and very personal space of your vehicle! How you drive, then, affects the safety of everyone on the road.

How are your driving habits and attitudes?

Just as poor behind the wheel habits and attitudes are hard to break, so, too, are safe, courteous, and responsible routines difficult to surrender. Restructure your driving techniques so that you become more confident on the road. Examine your perceptions of the driving experience and be receptive to positive changes. Whether you are a novice motorist or a veteran on the road, be open to correcting your driving deficiencies. These efforts take time and commitment, but success is on the horizon. *Behind the Wheel* suggests some easy to master skills on how to get into these safe and courteous driving rituals. Positive behind the wheel habits, coupled with a positive attitude, make for a contagious environment.

Turn the pages and learn how you can be the most confident and responsive driver possible.

Vehicle Maintenance and Servicing

Insights on Vehicle Checks

Regular preventative maintenance means repairing your automobile before a part breaks and further damages itself and other parts. By conducting automotive checks on a daily, weekly, monthly, biannual, and every two years basis, you help lower costly automotive repairs while reducing the risk of a collision. It is also advantageous to inspect your vehicle after lengthy trips or adverse weather and road conditions to be certain parts, such as the transmission, haven't been damaged.

A visual inspection remains a valid and easy way of maintaining your vehicle. Time checks are easier to remember than kilometre (mileage) checks. By getting into these time-framed, look-and-see habits, you are ensuring that your vehicle is reliable and safe. You are also acting in a smart and responsible manner.

Find a professional mechanic. If you prefer taking your vehicle to a dealership service centre, maintain an ongoing, positive relationship with a particular service representative. In the long run, you'll be a much more satisfied customer and proud owner of your vehicle, which means you'll take better care of it.

When talking with your mechanic or service representative, specify your vehicle's problems, rather than suggesting solutions. In other words, write down the symptoms - what noises and movements your vehicle makes, where the problem occurs, and when the malfunction happens. At the time the repair order is written, insist that the old parts (spark plugs, air filter, etc.) be left in the trunk so that you are assured a new part has been installed, and you can also see what a particular used part looks like. If you are unsure about the work completed, take your vehicle for a test drive after the repairs have been completed. Be comfortable with the repair bill; ask to have all charges explained.

Although tune-ups are recommended at certain kilometre (mileage) intervals, know what a tune-up entails. Most include changing the air filter, conducting a computerized analysis of the engine, checking all fluid levels, and inspecting the belts and hoses. But what about an oil and oil filter change? In most instances, you have to specifically request this procedure. You must also indicate if you want brakes inspected, tires rotated, and wiper blades replaced. Write down *everything* you want checked, repaired, and/or replaced on the work estimate.

For specific information on the regular maintenance schedules for your car or multi-purpose vehicle (minivan, light truck, or sport-utility vehicle), consult the owner's manual.

WOOO!! I FEEL SO IMPORTANT, HEH, HEH!

Daily Vehicle Checks

Prior to sitting behind the wheel, take one minute to visually inspect the outside of your vehicle by doing a "walk around."

- Look for body dents and broken lights
- Check that the licence plate is still on your vehicle
- Wipe dirty exterior lights
- Note tire inflation and tread wear
- Look for obstructions
- Look underneath for fluid spills

Weekly Vehicle Checks

Once a week checks take only 15 to 20 minutes. Park your vehicle on level ground with the engine cold.

- Fluid levels – check amount of engine oil and top up windshield washer reservoir
- Hoses - are any bulging, cracked, or mushy feeling?
- Interior and exterior lights – replace burned-out bulbs
- Wires - are any frayed?
- Tires – check air pressure and rub your hand across each tire to feel for bumps
- Tire inflation valves – replace broken or cracked valves
- Windshield wipers – clean rubber on the blades
- Electrical and ignition system - drive your vehicle at highway speeds (100 km/h [60 mph]) for 15 to 20 minutes every week to recharge the electrical system and clean out carbon build-up on the spark plugs.

Monthly Vehicle Maintenance and Servicing

On a monthly basis, inspect the following automotive parts. Remember to look under the hood when the engine is cold, except when you are checking the automatic transmission fluid level - the engine should be hot.

- Air filter – check if dirty
- Battery – check fluid level in cells
- Battery cables - are they secured to the battery posts and do the cables and posts have acid build-up?
- Batteries – test flashlight, remote trunk opener, etc.
- Belts, such as air conditioner, air pump, fan, and power steering - check for cracks, a shiny appearance, and amount of free play
- Engine block - are there oil leaks at the top of the engine?
- Engine oil – change oil and filter if oil is black
- Fan - are blades bent or broken?
- Fire extinguisher – check by reading the label on the side of the container

- Fluid levels - antifreeze in coolant reservoir (or radiator), automatic or manual transmission, brake fluid master cylinder, clutch fluid master cylinder, engine oil, power steering fluid, and windshield washer fluid – check quantity and quality
- Gas-line antifreeze - add 150 ml ($^2/_3$ c.) to gas tank to prevent moisture accumulation
- Horn - does it work?
- Parking brake – is the cable loose?
- Brake, clutch, and gas pedals - clean and test for ease of movement
- Radiator – look for leaks along the core seams and at the base of the two hoses where the clamps are
- Radiator cap - check springs and rubber seal
- Radiator hoses – do they feel soft or spongy?
- Shock absorbers – test by bouncing vehicle at each corner
- Spark plug wires – are they firmly attached to the spark plugs?
- Tires - check air pressure, including spare tire
- Tire treads – put a penny into treads
- Interior of vehicle – spot clean by wiping dashboard, reorganizing glove compartment, etc.
- Exterior of vehicle – wash, remembering to spray wash underneath

GIRLS, I'VE JUST HAD A MAKE OVER.
LOOK OUT NOW!

BiAnnual Vehicle Servicing

You can do the weekly and monthly vehicle inspections in the comfort of your yard, but other vehicle servicing is best left to a professional mechanic. The following outlines procedures you should have performed by a reputable mechanic twice a year.

- Air conditioning unit – check for leaks, refrigerant level, and strength
- Air filter – replace if dirty
- Antifreeze – test strength and check for leaks
- Battery – perform a battery test
- Body parts - lubricate all moving body parts (for example, door locks and hinges, glove and visor hinges, hood and trunk latches)
- Braking system - inspect system, such as amount of wear on pads and shoes
- Engine oil and oil filter – change oil and filter
- Exhaust system – examine parts, such as muffler and pipes and look for loose clamps and hangers
- Fuel filter - replace if clogged
- Fuel-injection system – conduct a computer systems check
- Headlights – adjust if aimed too high or low
- Hoses and belts - look for cracks, frays, and shiny appearances
- Parking brake - adjust cable if loose
- Pedals - test gas, brake, and clutch pedals for amount of play, worn-out parts, etc.
- Spark plugs – change all plugs if heavy carbon build-up at electrodes
- Suspension system – examine for loose CV- or U-joints, worn-out shocks, etc.
- Tires – rotate, depending on distance travelled in the last six months; decide if a wheel alignment is necessary
- Transmission system – check for leaks, quality and quantity of fluid, etc.
- Windshield wiper blades – change rubber, including rear wiper blade

Vehicle Servicing Every Two Years

By servicing your vehicle every two years, you are keeping it in tip-top shape, which means fewer costly repair bills. Plus, a well-maintained vehicle uses less gas. Prevention is the key word here.

The following outlines procedures a professional mechanic should perform.

- Automatic transmission - replace filter and fluid inside pan
- Brakes - inspect brakes at front and rear
- Brake fluid - flush old brake fluid and refill brake fluid master cylinder using silicone-based brake fluid for longer lasting fluid; otherwise, use regular brake fluid
- Fuel filter – install new filter
- Fuel-injection system - test sensors and other components of system
- Ignition system – check for electrical current, frayed wires, etc.
- Manual transmission pan – check oil for quality and quantity
- Radiator and cooling system – flush system and replace with 60/40 or 50/50 antifreeze mixture unless vehicle has extended-wear coolant
- Radiator hoses – change upper and lower hoses and install new clamps at their ends
- Spark plugs and spark plug wires – change all spark plugs and wires
- Thermostat – change thermostat and gasket

Pre-Driving Habits

Before You Get Inside Your Vehicle

- Conduct the daily checks noted in the preceding page.

- Ask yourself if you are mentally alert and physically able to get behind the wheel. Do you have vision or hearing limitations which would restrict you from seeing low light in the evenings or hearing an ambulance siren?

- Always wear footwear when driving. There may be legal implications if you don't.

- Is your trip planned? Highway driving, with its high speeds, traffic volume, and numerous information signs in major cities, requires advance preparation. Know your route numbers and which direction you will be travelling. Always ask yourself, "Do I know how to get to where I want to go?"

- Can you consolidate trips? For example, rather than three or four grocery trips per week, plan for one or two.

- Before travelling on unfamiliar city streets, look on a map and note two street names just prior to your destination's street. That way, you'll be able to safely slow down before your turn, rather than braking suddenly.

- Have lots of coins safely and readily accessible for parking meters and toll booths.

- The fastest way to get the engine warm is to slowly start driving after the ignition has been on for one minute. Research shows that it takes about 5 km (3 mi.) for an engine to warm up, longer when it's colder outside. If the engine stalls, it indicates a problem under the hood.

Once In The Driver's Seat

- Immediately lock all doors.

- Wipe your feet on the floor mat. This reduces the chance of your foot slipping off the pedal if the bottom of your shoe is wet.

- Secure loose objects inside your vehicle.

- Have a map or directions beside you with paper and a not-too-sharp pencil handy.

- If you insist on using a cellular phone, have it accessible and turned on.

- Adjust the climate control settings and vents.

- Adjust the seat and head restraint.

- Adjust all mirrors (rear-view and driver and passenger side-view mirrors).

- Adjust the steering wheel if it has a tilt feature.

- Fasten your seat belt and make sure all occupants have fastened theirs.

- Turn ignition key to "on." To avoid engine and transmission damage, let the engine warm up for one minute before slowly driving away.

- Check indicator lights and gauges on the dashboard. For example, does the fuel gauge register more than one-half?

- Set the radio to your favourite station or put in a cassette or CD. Secure beside you the other cassettes or CDs you want to listen to. Using headphones while driving is illegal.

- Depending on the weather, adjust the heater or air conditioner, or open the windows and sunroof.

- Release the parking brake, keeping your foot on the brake.

- Signal your intention to pull away and shoulder check before leaving your parking spot. You can also give a short toot of the horn to let people know your intention. As a courtesy, give a wave to those who have accommodated you.

Driving Habits

City vs. Highway Driving

City Driving

> City driving involves many stops and starts. Although speed limits are usually around 50 km/h (30 mph), there are many distractions - pedestrians, other motorists making unexpected turns, or traffic lights. Look all around you - to both sides and the rear of your vehicle, as well as to the front. Your ability to make quick decisions in a busy environment reflects on how aware you are of your surroundings.

> Always have a planned alternative route, including one to and from work. Construction, collisions, and unexpected traffic volume can cause lengthy delays.

I GOTTA PULL OVER!!
I'M STARTING TO SEE FUZZY CARS

- ➤ Downtown activities mean lots of potential for pedestrian accidents. Be on the lookout for jaywalkers, people making last-minute dashes against the "don't walk" sign, and individuals running to or from a bus.

- ➤ Shopping centres and parking lots have vehicles and people travelling in many different directions. Although your vehicle is moving at slow speeds, be on the lookout for activity in this busy environment.

- ➤ The suburbs house families. Expect the unexpected, such as children and pets running across the street. Toys in driveways indicate a child has been using them recently and could still be around. Look for kids on bikes and skateboards - they are too preoccupied to watch the road themselves.

Highway Driving

- ➤ Highways and freeways prohibit slow-moving vehicles. Pedestrian traffic is non-existent, except in emergency situations. The higher speeds of highways and freeways require you to make quick decisions within a fast-changing environment. Special driving techniques are also required, such as merging on entering ramps.

> Be aware of "highway hypnosis" - the constant sounds of the engine humming, tires moving, and wind blowing can, and usually do, make you drowsy.

> Driving tests reveal that less gas is used when you maintain a speed 10 km (6 mph) less than the posted speed limit. Using cruise control also reduces gas consumption. Set the cruise control at 1 km (1 mph) below the speed you want to cruise at.

> Statistics indicate that you save only about five minutes when driving for 100 km (60 mph) at 115 km/h (70 mph) vs. driving the same distance at 100 km/h (60 mph). That extra 15 km/h (10 mph) shows you are probably exceeding the speed limit and reducing your chances of maintaining control of your vehicle.

Day vs. Night Driving

Day Driving

> To improve visibility for you and other drivers during the daytime, activate the low beams, rather than relying on daytime running lights.

> The sun or glare from snow can reduce visibility during daylight hours. Adjust the sun visor and wear high-quality sunglasses with grey or green lenses that are free from scratches.

COOL, EH !!

➤ For most people, their internal body clock slows down between 2:00 p.m. - 5:00 p.m. Avoid prolonged driving during this period.

Night Driving

➤ With the sun setting below the horizon, light is limited. Your eyes must adapt to the darkness at the sides and the lights in front and behind. Never wear sunglasses at dusk or during the night.

➤ At night, artificial and natural lights affect your depth perception (how close or how far an object is).

➤ Low beams are mandatory one hour before dusk to one hour after dawn. The specific times vary depending on the time of year.

➤ Switch from high to low beams when oncoming traffic approaches or when there are vehicles directly in front of you. Know what the law dictates with regards to the distance for switching from high to low beams for oncoming traffic.

➤ Use the night switch on the rear-view mirror when night driving in heavy traffic.

➤ Turn the dashboard lights down to reduce interior light glare.

SUN DOWN !
SUN GLASSES UP!

➤ Angle the side-view mirrors down a bit to reduce the glare of lights from other vehicles.

➤ Most people have an internal body clock that slows down between 2:00 a.m. - 6:00 a.m. Avoid getting behind the wheel at this time.

➤ Drive approximately 10 km/h (6 mph) slower at night.

HEY, HE'S CUTE. AND, I JUST HAPPEN TO HAVE A CELL PHONE. IS THIS FATE, OR WHAT?

Distractions While Driving

Cellular phones

• Cell phones are now an integral part of communication while behind the wheel. No matter how good a driver you are, though, phone conversations affect your concentration as you manoeuvre through traffic.

• With so much cell phone use, governments are gathering statistics relating cell phone use while driving with collisions. Governments in some counties are taking the initiative by banning the use of a cell phone while driving.

• To ease this tension between driving and talking on the cell phone, here are a few tips:

➤ Commit to using the cell phone only in the city, but pull over to talk on it. Highways are off limits for cell phone usage - you are driving too fast and cannot easily pull over to the side.

➤ If the phone rings while you are driving, let the voicemail take the message - that's what it is for.

➤ Have your passenger use the cell phone instead of you. Older kids often relish the opportunity to use this fun technology.

➤ Know your cell phone and its features, such as how to dial, what button to press for an incoming call, and how to operate the speed dial.

➤ Pre-program frequently called numbers so that you don't have to dial them while driving.

➤ If a number is not in memory, dial two numbers, watch traffic, dial two more numbers, watch traffic, and so on.

➤ Never look up phone numbers or take notes while driving. Invest in an inexpensive electronic organizer. It readily provides you with telephone numbers.

➤ Always keep your head up and eyes on the road while talking on the phone.

➤ Put the cell phone safely within reach. Invest in an inexpensive cellular phone holding unit so you can talk hands-free. (However, research does show that hands-free cell phones offer no additional safety benefits over hand-held models). The one advantage of a hands-free cell phone is that both your hands stay on the steering wheel, which means you maintain better control of your vehicle.

➤ Avoid stressful conversations while talking on the cell phone.

➤ Avoid making unnecessary telephone calls, such as letting your husband know you'll be home in ten minutes. Keep conversations brief and to the point.

➤ Let the person you are talking with know you are driving.

➤ If driving conditions become hazardous, cut off the conversation.

Children

• Children can take your attention away from the task at hand – driving. To keep kids from "driving you crazy" while behind the wheel, occupy them with toys and activities they can engage in while confined to the child-restraint seat. Mothers have a knack for being creative - plan games and other activities for the kids, especially on long trips. Shorter drives provide an ideal opportunity for conversation as kids love to talk about themselves. Sometimes it is just a matter of taking their shoes, socks, and coat off (weather permitting) to keep them comfortable. Motion sickness is common with kids so watch for the sun glaring through the rear windows.

Eating

- Eating while driving is a safety hazard. If you do, make sure the food you consume does not ooze or fall apart while driving. For example, it is better to eat a plain ham sandwich than a hamburger complete with lettuce, mustard, pickles, and onions on a sesame seed bun.

Smoking

- If you smoke while driving, butt out your cigarette in the ashtray, rather than throwing it out the window. A lit cigarette can cause a brush fire, especially if the landscape is dry.

Other Distractions

- Applying makeup, trying to secure your (or an occupant's) seat belt, and searching for coins for the toll both, are three more examples of distractions that affect your ability to drive safely and responsibly.
- If you are unfamiliar with the road and area, avoid looking at a map while driving. Instead, safely pull over to the roadside to focus on where you are and where you want to go.

Driver Exercises

To combat fatigue when delayed in traffic, safely perform the following exercises:

Deep Breathing

- Sit straight, breathe in, then exhale and relax your body.

Neck Bends

- Move your neck right and left, so that the right ear reaches the right shoulder and the left ear reaches the left shoulder.

Neck Rotations

- Slowly rotate your head right and then left.

Shoulder Movement

- Move both shoulders forward and then backward.

Shoulder Shrugs

- Shrug both shoulders to your ears and then relax them.

Foot Circulation

- Take one shoe off to wake up your foot and improve circulation (cool air refreshes your foot and toes). Keep in mind; however, that some provinces (states) mandate that shoes must be worn while driving.

Drunk Drivers

- Road rage is prevalent everywhere nowadays. An erratic driver may be drunk or someone with a very bad attitude. Make sure you don't ever become one of those drunk or angry motorists.

- Phone the local police, RCMP (Highway Patrol), or 911 if you witness erratic driver behaviours such as:

  - Excessive weaving

  - Driving at high or inconsistent speeds

  - Disregarding lights, stop signs, and other traffic-control devices

  - Driving at night without headlights

  - Driving in cold weather with the windows open

- Provide law enforcement authorities with the following information:
  - Licence plate number
  - Physical characteristics of the vehicle (make, colour, etc.)
  - Physical characteristics of the driver
  - Time you noticed the erratic behaviour
  - Location of the erratic driver (be as specific as possible)
- What about family members and friends?
  - When your teenager has the family car, she or he should be explicit about their intentions. Letting you know the destination and expected time of return is a part of driving intelligently. Inform everyone that a phone call places no expectations or draws no criticisms.
  - Being a friend to someone who is drunk may mean taking aggressive steps to make sure she or he does not get behind the wheel. You may even have to grab the keys and run.
  - You do have a choice by saying "NO!" to being a passenger of a drunk driver. Ask yourself, "Am I willing to die for this individual?"
  - Decide on a designated driver before you start socializing. If you will be the one consuming alcohol, leave your vehicle door and ignition keys with someone you trust.

Eye Movement, Shoulder Checking, and Signalling

Eye Movement

  - Your driving depends primarily on your vision. Statistics indicate that more than 90% of what happens on the road is affected by your ability to see. "See" that you maintain regular eye checkups.
  - Keep your eyes constantly moving. Be aware of what is around you, not just what is in front. For example, do you notice a parked vehicle idling and someone in the driver's seat? This motorist may suddenly move her or his vehicle into your path.
  - Drive with your eyes looking well ahead, rather than focusing on what is directly in front of your vehicle or watching only the vehicle ahead.
  - Always maintain eye contact with the road, even when engaged in conversation with passengers.

- ➤ Frequently glance in the rear-view mirror – five to eight seconds is the recommended frequency.

- ➤ Periodically glance at the gauges and lights on the dashboard; don't stare at them.

- ➤ Be aware of your peripheral vision. What happens to your sides is just as important as what takes place ahead of and behind your vehicle. Periodically glance at the side-view mirrors. Keep in mind those blind spots, especially when changing lanes.

- ➤ At stop signs, just before unmarked intersections, at railway crossings, and after a traffic light turns green, always scan left, look centre, scan right, look centre, and, finally, scan left again before proceeding.

WELL, MR. RACY FACE.
WE'RE IN QUITE A HURRY,
AREN'T WE?

Shoulder Checking

- ➤ Always shoulder check once the turn-signal arm has been activated.

- ➤ Shoulder check before you begin to move your vehicle into another lane.

- ➤ Use your head to shoulder check, rather than your upper body. If you move your body, your hands on the steering wheel gravitate in the same direction.

Signaling

➤ Use the turn signal before changing lanes, turning, passing another vehicle, entering or leaving a highway, and starting from a parked position.

➤ Make sure the signal arm has disengaged after your vehicle has made the indicated move.

➤ Signal well in advance to let all drivers and pedestrians around you know your intention to turn. Do not signal too soon, especially if there is another possible turn before the turn you intend to take.

➤ Know that there are laws with regards to signaling. For example, some laws dictate that 30 m (100 ft.) is the required distance to signal when driving in urban centres. On highways, the legal minimum distance is 100 m (350 ft.). Whatever the distance, signalling is the law.

➤ In an emergency situation, always signal your intention to pull over to the side of the road.

➤ If the turn signals do not work, use hand signals to indicate your intention. Note that there is a difference between hand *signals* and hand *gestures*. Never gesture with your hand for another motorist to do something as you can be held legally accountable if a collision occurs. The following are standard hand signals the driver should use:

▪ Left-hand turn signal – left arm and hand extended straight out

▪ Right-hand turn signal – left arm bent up at the elbow, with the hand pointing up

▪ Stopping or slowing down – left arm bent down at the elbow, with the hand pointing down

RED LIGHT, MOVE RIGHT.
LET MR. OFFICER DO
HIS JOB

Traffic Laws, Control Devices, and Road Signs

- Traffic laws were put in place for a reason - everyone's safety. There may be that one time, though, when you must make a split-second decision to break the law to avoid a collision.

- Traffic-control lights indicate stop (red); proceed, but with caution (green); and get ready to stop or clear the intersection (yellow). Most yellow lights stay on for about six seconds.

- Speed limits are just that – maximum speeds in ideal weather and road conditions. Know your limits, taking into consideration your behind the wheel abilities.

- While provincial (state) governments dictate speed limits in school zones, city bylaws may specify different times that the law is in effect. Note also all-year schools. They are usually indicated by "All Year School" on the sign, along with the times the speed limit is in effect.

- Highway and city signs are designed for easy comprehension, with the symbols reading from the bottom up, and words reading from left to right, top to bottom. Signs come in different colours and shapes and fall into three categories: information/guidance, regulatory, and warning.

- Not only must you read traffic signs; you need to understand what they mean. There are signs common around the world, but variations do occur within each country.

Weather and Road Conditions

- When driving in ideal weather and road conditions, use the two-second rule in urban areas and four-second rule on highways for the distance between your vehicle and the one in front of you. As weather and road conditions deteriorate, increase the time (pavement) between you and the vehicle ahead.

- Take the necessary precautions when driving in the four seasons. Winter driving requires extra attention to ice- and snow-covered roads, while summer driving may mean your vehicle will overheat if the antifreeze is not sufficient in quantity and strength.

- Fog, heavy rain, sand-storms, and blowing snow all reduce visibility when driving. Adjust your speed accordingly.

- When driving in strong winds, crosswinds can make your vehicle wander. Ensure you have a firm grip on the steering wheel to maintain control.

- Reduce your driving speed when at high altitudes. Your reaction time slows down with a decrease in oxygen.

- When travelling through the prairies or in hot weather, always carry drinking water - an adult needs an average of 1 L (1 qt.) of water per day to survive.

- Hydroplaning happens when the tires ride on top of water-soaked roads, especially during heavy rainfall. When the tires lose all contact with the road surface, skidding can occur. Ease up on the gas pedal if your vehicle is hydroplaning; putting your foot on the brake pedal can cause you to lose control of your vehicle. Keep in mind that hydroplaning isn't necessarily associated with speed. If your vehicle has low tire pressure or poor tire tread, or if there are water-filled ruts in the road, hydroplaning can happen at low speeds.

- To avoid an electrical short, turn off all electrical accessories, such as air conditioner, lights, and radio, when driving through deep water.

- Avoid driving in water deeper than half the height of the tires as water can enter the brakes and transmission, causing your vehicle to stall.

- It takes less than 0.6 m (2 ft.) of water to move a vehicle. Be also aware of flooding conditions.

- Once a vehicle hits a body of water, it takes three to five minutes to sink (see *Troubleshooting:* "Scenarios - What To Do").

- When driving through mud or puddles and on snow-covered roads, reduce your speed and follow the tracks left by the previous vehicle. Make sure the tracks go where you want to go, and that they don't lead you off the road.

- Rain or snow can result in your vehicle's windshield constantly being sprayed with mud and slush. Keep a full reservoir of washer fluid.

- As temperatures rise, road surfaces often become slippery, especially if there has been overnight frost.

- Winter road conditions usually mean ice- and snow-covered roads. Allow yourself more time to get where you are going and reduce your speed.

- Roads can get more black ice when the temperature hovers around 9°C (48°F) than when it is −10°C (+14°F).

- Light snow or freezing rain makes roads icy very quickly. As a precaution, stop well behind other vehicles at intersections. Once stopped, slowly move forward to reduce the gap between you and the vehicle in front.

- After driving on a winter day, leave a side window open a crack. This prevents the insides of the windows from fogging up when you next start your vehicle. If parking outside, make sure the open window doesn't face the wind.

- Clear snow from your vehicle before driving. Snow left on your vehicle can enter the interior via the outside grille, which causes the inside windows to fog. Snow blowing off your vehicle also reduces visibility for other motorists.

- Be aware of road design (e.g., curves), surface material (e.g., blacktop, concrete, dirt, gravel), and surface conditions (e.g., bumps, ice, holes, mud, oil, puddles). They all affect driving ability.

- Road lanes are closer together in tunnels. Adjust your speed and always put your low beams on when driving through a tunnel.

- If you are unsure of a narrow and unfamiliar bridge, especially in a rural area, walk on the bridge before you drive across it.

- Elevated bridges and ramps freeze first because the cold air sits both below and above them.

- Trees and buildings often shade roads. This is where ice first builds up, and the shade tends to keep these areas frozen.

- A wet road is most slick when rain first hits the pavement. Wet leaves also make the road more slippery. Reduce your speed by about 10 km/h (6 mph) when roads are wet.

- Spring temperatures often bring potholes to the roads. You can damage your vehicle's suspension and tires from driving over a deep pothole. As well, the front wheels often go out of alignment after driving over potholes.

- Curves are especially dangerous when the road is wet because they can get very slippery, especially when it's raining or snowing.

Post-Driving Habits

Parking

- Always set the parking brake. Remember that the parking brake cable can break when the outside temperature is below 10°C (+14°F).

- On cold, windy days, park your vehicle with the engine facing away from the wind. This prevents the engine from freezing due to direct wind exposure.

- When parking on level ground, straighten the front tires. Tires left at a sharp angle can damage the power steering system, especially in cold weather.

- If you are going to be away from your vehicle for more than one minute, turn the ignition key to "off," rather than letting the engine idle in "P." This saves fuel.

- Do not keep the engine running in confined areas, such as a garage. Carbon monoxide fumes can enter the interior of your vehicle.

- Turn the front tires at an angle when parking on a hill with or without a curb. Make sure you set the parking brake.

OOPS, SORRY!

HEY, WATCH WHERE
YOU'RE SWINGING THAT
THING

Before You Leave Your Vehicle

- Turn off the headlights.
- Turn off all interior accessories, such as the radio.
- Close windows, including the sunroof.
- Turn the ignition key to "off."
- Keep all valuables hidden.
- Take the ignition key with you.
- Shoulder check before opening the door. You are responsible if your open door hits a vehicle, cyclist, or pedestrian.
- Lock all doors.
- Young adults or pets should never be left unattended inside your vehicle.

Other Road Traffic

Animals

- Pets can unexpectedly run across the street. Be extra cautious when driving through residential areas.
- Never feed wild animals, especially from the shoulder of the highway because this entices them to continue wandering onto the road for food.
- When travelling through federal and provincial (state) parks, watch for wild animals roaming onto the roads, especially at dawn and dusk.
- Be on the lookout for livestock, such as cattle, horses, and sheep, when driving on rural roads.
- Pay attention to animal-crossing signs.

Bicycles

- Although children should be taught the laws of bicycle riding, they generally lack the experience to always remember and obey the rules. Children are also unpredictable.
- Be aware of children on oversized bikes. Their ability to handle the bike is greatly reduced.

- Your vehicle often creates a wind stream that can cause a cyclist to lose her or his balance. Reduce your speed when passing cyclists.

- Potholes, gravel, or other obstructions, at the road's edge can alter a cyclist's path. Be aware that a cyclist may unexpectedly move left.

- Never honk your horn when passing a cyclist; you can startle her or him.

- Never pass a cyclist if there is an oncoming vehicle. Let the vehicle go by you and then move slightly left to pass the cyclist.

Buses - School, Motor Coach, City

- Children do not have the same understanding of traffic laws as adults. Once off the bus, they may run across the road without warning.

- A school bus that has a flashing amber light means it is about to stop. Slow down and be prepared to stop.

- When the school bus has flashing red lights, you must stop, regardless which direction you are driving (except on a divided highway, if you are driving in the opposite direction of the school bus).

- City bus passengers may unexpectedly run across the street to catch the bus or they could head in any direction after leaving the bus.

- Maintain a safe distance behind motorcoach buses, especially on hills. These types of buses require longer braking times than passenger vehicles.

THANKS, HANDSOME, FOR LETTING ME PASS YA

Emergency Vehicles

- In urban areas, move to the right when you see a red or blue flashing light on an emergency vehicle. On highways and one-way streets, try to move to the right, rather than the left.

- Immediately signal your intention to change lanes, shoulder check, and then safely pull over to allow the ambulance, fire truck, or police cruiser a safe and open thoroughfare.

Passenger Vehicles

- Other motorists may not have safe, courteous, and responsible driving habits. Many drivers are often unpredictable.

- Always put some pavement between you and other motorists. This gives you increased reaction time, the precious seconds needed to avoid a collision.

- If you experience a tailgater, ease up on your gas pedal, rather than applying the brakes. Most likely, the impatient motorist will pass you.

- When passing parked vehicles, be cautious of children and pets, who often run from between them, or a driver inside one of these vehicles who may open the door unexpectedly.

- Sport-utility vehicles (SUVs) are larger than most passenger vehicles. Driving one takes getting used to its extra weight and size.

Passing Vehicles

- It is illegal to exceed the posted speed limit when passing another vehicle.

- Always obey the pavement markings when passing. For example, a solid yellow line on your side of the centreline means you cannot pass.

- Carefully judge the speed and distance of an oncoming vehicle if you are considering passing.

- Use the left turn signal to indicate to the vehicle in front that you want to pass, even if driving on a two-lane highway. You can also flash your headlights once to alert the driver that you are about to pass.

- To judge the distance between you and the vehicle you are passing, look in the rear-view and passenger side-view mirrors, and then shoulder check. Use your right turn signal to indicate your intention to return to the right lane.

- When in doubt, it is safer not to pass at all.

- Be sure the motorist behind you is not moving to pass you at the same time you are intending to pass the vehicle in front.

- Assist motorists who are passing you by slowing down and allowing them to safely move in front of you. Ultimately, you are also protecting yourself.

Pedestrians

- Pedestrians are difficult to see if they are wearing dark clothes, especially at night.

- Older persons do not have the same reflexes as younger adults and their vision can be limited.

- Handicapped persons may not have the same awareness or physical abilities to, for example, move quickly across the street.

- Children have not yet developed the capacity to judge time and space. Also, their hearing and vision are not fully developed. In other words, children can be unpredictable.

- Animals (pets and wildlife) are also unpredictable.

- As a pedestrian, educate yourself on the pedestrian rules of the road. Cross the street only at designated crosswalks. Although you have the legal right of way, always look both ways before crossing the street. Walk on the side of the road facing traffic when there are no sidewalks. Wear brightly coloured clothes, especially at dawn, dusk, and late at night.

Semi-Trailers

- Most collisions with semis are the result of someone following too closely behind a semi-trailer. Its size alone should deter you from staying too close to its rear-end.

- Use the four-second rule when driving behind a semi - there should be at least four seconds of distance between you and the semi in front. In other words, keep lots of pavement between you and the semi-trailer.

- If you can't see the truck driver's face in one of her or his side-view mirrors, the semi driver cannot see you. You *want* that driver to know where you are.

HEY, BIG GUY, BE MY
GUEST, DON'T LET
ME STOP YOU

- Passing a semi is different than passing a passenger vehicle. It takes longer to pass a semi and its weight often acts as suction, pulling your vehicle towards it.

- After passing a semi, leave lots of pavement between you and the semi. You don't want the truck driver to have to put on the brakes.

- Always avoid passing a semi on the right.

- Do not use semi-trailers as windbreaks as you cannot see the road in front of you because the semi blocks your view.

- Semis have a different braking system than passenger vehicles. Maintain a safe distance when driving behind a semi, especially on hills.

- Semis can roll back when stopping. Maintain a distance between you and the semi-trailer when parking behind one.

Trains

- Slow down at railway crossings, listen for train whistles, and look both ways before you cross, even if the warning lights or crossing gate are not activated - they may not be working.

- If the railway-signal lights are activated or the crossing gate is lowered, stop well behind the crossing. There are legal minimum distances from the crossing to where you stop.

- Watch out for a second train approaching, possibly in the opposite direction if there are double railway tracks.

- Never shift gears on a railway crossing.

- Never pass another vehicle just before a railway crossing; there are legal minimum distances.

- If your vehicle stalls on railway tracks and you can see a train approaching or hear its whistle, immediately leave your vehicle. Run alongside the tracks towards the train so that flying debris won't injure you – once the train hits your vehicle, objects will be pushed ahead of, rather than behind the train.

- If your vehicle stalls on railway tracks and you can't see a train or hear a whistle, display reflectors on the tracks in both directions. Put the reflectors far enough down the tracks to give the conductor ample warning. Try to move your vehicle off the tracks, but always be on the lookout for a train. Remember that a train requires a lot of track to stop, even when the brakes are on.

- Commuter trains require the same respect as other trains. Never drive over the tracks when the crossing gate is lowered or the warning lights are flashing. Keep in mind many tracks are built in two's so a second train could be coming along the other track.

Collisions

- *AutoTalk for Women* refers to "collisions" and not "accidents" in the belief that there are no such things as accidents.

- There are four types of vehicle collisions: frontal, side impact, rear, and rollovers. Although each collision affects your vehicle differently, keeping your seat belt on reduces the risk of injury no matter where and how you are hit.

- Statistics indicate that more than 50% of all collisions occur within a 50 km (30 mph) radius of one's home, and at speeds less than 60 km/h (40 mph). Pay special attention when driving in your neighbourhood.

- Loose objects inside your vehicle can become deadly items. A tissue box on the back window ledge, a loose pencil, or a sharp toy can cause serious harm to you and any passenger when a high-speed collision occurs.

- Minimize the potential for a collision by always keeping lots of pavement between you and other road traffic.

- If a collision from the front looks imminent, flash your headlights, honk your horn, steer right (to avoid oncoming traffic), put your foot on the brake pedal, and try to be hit at an angle, rather than head-on.

- If a collision from the rear looks imminent, apply the brakes, quickly steer to the right (to avoid your vehicle moving into the line of oncoming traffic or hitting a vehicle in front of you) and put your head firmly against the head restraint.

- If a collision to the side looks imminent, hold your hands firmly on the steering wheel (to stay in control of the spin) and try to have the other vehicle hit your vehicle's back corner. This takes quick-thinking and fast reflexes.

- If a collision looks inevitable, always choose to hit a vehicle, rather than a cyclist or pedestrian.

- For a collision report, see *AutoTalk Assistant*.

- If you hit an unoccupied vehicle, you are legally responsible (see *AutoTalk Assistant*).

Driving Solo

- Trust your instincts. Your body shows signs that something is not right by perspiring on the face and palms. Prepare yourself - get the baseball bat from under the driver's seat; be willing to hit the attacker's eyes, nose, and groin; get psyched up to yell "NO!" from the pit of your stomach.

- If you are accosted, vocals can offer a quick deterrent. Be as loud as possible – scream obscenities, yell "NO!" or use whatever words you need to use to attract attention. Shaking your finger or waving your hands while yelling can also deter a potential attacker.

- While walking to your vehicle, look at your surroundings to see if anyone is lingering around. Have the door and ignition keys in your hand, rather than looking for them in your purse once at your vehicle. Hold the door key so that it can be readily inserted into the lock. You can also use the pointed end to poke an intruder in the eyes.

- Inside your vehicle, keep a small Swiss Army knife handy. For example, push it between the front seat and backrest. Underneath the front seat, you may want to place a child-sized baseball bat.

- Before you open the driver's door, quickly look in the back seat to make sure no one is hiding.

- Once in the driver's seat, lock the doors and look around for suspicious looking vehicle occupants.

- Once you start driving, notice any unusual movements of other vehicles. Drive to a public place if someone is following you.

- After you park in your garage, stay in your vehicle until the garage door is closed.

- If your vehicle is lightly rear-ended, stay in it. Keep the doors locked and roll down the window a crack. Inform the other driver she or he should follow you, and then drive to a police station or a well-lit area with lots of people. Only when you feel safe should you get out of your vehicle and exchange information.

- When driving on highways and secondary roads, get into the habit of noting where the last gas station was in terms of distance or time as it relates to your specific location.

- Never pick up hitchhikers.

- When stopping at banking machines or convenience stores, look at who is lingering around before you get out of your vehicle. Drive through banking machines warrant the same caution even though you stay in the driver's seat.

- Some women dress "incognito" (for example, a baseball cap with hair tucked under, no bright makeup, such as lipstick, and shirt collar turned up) if they are driving solo at night or in an unfamiliar area.

MY GENERIC LOOK.
YA KNOW, I KINDA LIKE IT.

- It is never safe to sleep in your vehicle. If you decide to do so, stop in a well-lit area, lock all doors, roll down one window a crack to let in air, and keep the parking lights on. Stretch and get some fresh air once you awaken.

- If you must stop at a highway exit or entrance ramp, park your vehicle directly below a lighted lamp so that other motorists can see your vehicle.

- If your vehicle becomes disabled:

  ➤ and someone offers to help, open your window only enough to hear the person. Ask the individual to call a tow-truck company, or the police.

  ➤ never unlock your door or get in the vehicle of a stranger. The exception is a police officer, but ask for proper identification first.

  ➤ and you insist on getting in a stranger's vehicle or even in the vehicle of someone you know, write down pertinent information and leave it on the dashboard of your vehicle, not on the outside windshield (see *AutoTalk Assistant*). Lock all the doors of your disabled vehicle.

  ➤ and you have a cell phone, let your family know of your exact location and what the problem is. Then phone the police or towing company. Continue to update your family on what is happening.

  ➤ and it is daytime, assess the situation. Are you on a busy highway or on an unfamiliar city street? Even though it is light, you can still become caught in a dangerous situation. Use common sense. For example, change a flat tire only if you are comfortable with the procedure. If your battery is discharged, be at ease with who is offering to help you boost it.

  ➤ and it is nighttime, you have a number of choices:

    ■ Stay inside your vehicle with the doors locked until a police cruiser or tow truck stops.

    ■ Leave your vehicle and start walking. First, place a note on the dashboard and not on the outside windshield (see *AutoTalk Assistant*).

    ■ Get out of your vehicle and hide near it until a police cruiser arrives.

    ■ Try to fix what's caused your vehicle to stop running. Keep in mind it is difficult to see what's under the hood and around your vehicle at night, even if you use the headlights and a flashlight.

Thefts and Vandalism

- Roll up all windows and lock all doors when your vehicle is parked, even if you are making only a quick stop.

- Secure garage windows and doors; many vehicles are stolen from inside a home garage.

- Always take the ignition key with you.

- Given an option, park in well-lit areas where there are people.

- Ask a trusted neighbour to watch out for your vehicle. Extend the same courtesy by keeping an eye on her or his vehicle.

- Store valuables, including shopping bags, in the trunk or cover them with a heavy blanket.

- Carry with you at all times a colour photograph of your vehicle, along with pertinent information (see *AutoTalk Assistant*). In the event of a theft, the police have a picture of your vehicle, along with all its relevant information. Have your insurance company keep a photograph of your vehicle as well.

- Immediately call the police and your insurance company if a theft or vandalism occurs. Provide them with particulars, such as location, damage, what was taken, etc.

I'M NOT PARANOID, JUST BEING CAUTIOUS. PEOPLE CAN GET WEIRD WHEN THERE'S MONEY INVOLVED

- Some police stations and automobile clubs offer a complimentary window decal that alerts police your vehicle is not to be on the road between 1:00 a.m. - 5:00 a.m. The police will stop anyone driving your vehicle during this time.

- Satellite-based tracking systems, electronic ignition-interruption systems (two keys are needed to start the vehicle), talking perimeter systems, theft- deterrent systems with a personal panic mode, and secret codes and passwords are the latest high-tech systems used to combat vehicle theft.

- Anti-theft security systems offer protection from vandalism, but they usually fail to deter automobile thieves. If someone really wants your vehicle, it will be stolen.

- Expensive vehicles are not necessarily the most frequently stolen vehicles. Provincial (state) auto-theft tastes vary. For example, the Prairies report a high number of trucks stolen, whereas the West Coast see more thefts of exotic vehicles.

- Automotive thieves are sophisticated. Some have their own tow trailers. For others, auto theft is just one part of their crime "portfolio."

Vacations

Before You Head Out

- Plan your trip. You don't want to be caught kilometres (miles) from the next service centre, restaurant, bathroom, town, or city. You also don't want to be tired trying to make it to the next motel, campsite, or safe rest area. Keep a detailed highway map handy. Have one passenger, who is able to translate what's on the map to where you are driving, act as navigator.

- Keep a photo of your vehicle and pertinent information in your wallet (see *AutoTalk Assistant*). This information is vital if your vehicle is stolen.

- Record credit card numbers and the numbers to call if they are stolen. Keep this information in a place other than your wallet, but it needs to be quickly available.

- Leave your travel itinerary with someone you trust.

- Take traveller checks, rather than cash.

- Do you or one of your passengers experience motion sickness? Adult herbal remedies include chewing ginger or taking ginger capsules, drinking peppermint tea, eating peppermint candies, or wearing acupressure wristbands.

- Tune up your vehicle before vacations to help avoid unexpected costs and frustrations.

- When travelling during the warmer months, install a bug deflector at the front of your vehicle.

- Border crossing requires additional documentation:

  ➤ A valid passport for all vehicle occupants, or other proof of citizenship

  ➤ An updated vaccination certificate if travelling with an animal

  ➤ The vehicle registration and insurance

  ➤ An inventory of all personal belongings - this provides customs officials with an accessible, itemized list, including all liquor and tobacco products

  ➤ Permits for firearms

  ➤ Declaration of purchases made in the visiting country, including receipts - the more detailed and organized you are, the less time you are likely to spend at the border

Home Checklist

- See *AutoTalk Assistant*

Securing Your Luggage

- Use ID tags. List only your first name and telephone number on the inside and exterior of all pieces of luggage, rather than your full name with street address and city or town.

- Note the maximum payload capacity (passenger, rack, luggage, and other cargo) outlined in the vehicle owner's manual.

- Overloading your vehicle promotes engine overheating and damage to the suspension system.

- Load your vehicle so that the bulk of the weight is at the front, including passenger weight.

- Load the roof rack with heavier items at the bottom and centre and lighter items on top.

- Do not pile luggage and other cargo higher than the front and rear seat back so that your view will be obstructed. Loose luggage is also a safety hazard if a sudden stop or collision occurs.

- Exhaust fumes can enter the interior of your vehicle if you leave the trunk open while driving.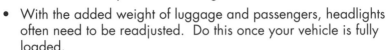

- With the added weight of luggage and passengers, headlights often need to be readjusted. Do this once your vehicle is fully loaded.

Trailer Towing

- Trailer towing requires special skills. Learn how to safely back up and turn corners. Practise these manoeuvres in a large parking lot after hours or take a course on towing a trailer behind your vehicle.

- Make sure your vehicle has the capacity to tow a trailer and that the hitch can hold the weight of the trailer.

- The law dictates that the trailer must have working brake and signal lights. Its safety-chain hitch must be securely crossed and fastened. Wiring from the vehicle to the trailer should never be frayed.

- Load the trailer so that the bulk of the weight is at the front and is equally distributed on the right and left sides. Secure all items. Once loaded, your vehicle and trailer should be balanced so that neither their front nor rear is closer to the ground.

SURE GLAD I TOOK THAT CLASS ON PULLING TRAILERS. IT'S A SNAP!!

OH BOY! OH BOY! VACATION TIME.
I'M READY, I'M READY, UH-HUH, LET'S GO,
LET'S GO!

- Ensure that the spare tire fits the trailer wheels.

- Close the trailer's roof vent and windows before you begin driving.

- On a daily basis, test the trailer's tire pressures and rear lights.

- When towing a trailer on the highway, avoid soft shoulders where the trailer can easily wander off the road.

Vacationing with Kids

- Teach your children one important in-the-vehicle safety rule - always keep the seat belt on and in the correct position (shoulder belt over the chest and lap belt across the hips).

- Children often get frustrated when rushed. Look at the driving experience as part of your family vacation. Enjoy the "getting there" as much as the final destination. You can accomplish this in a number of creative ways:

  ➤ Make the rear seat of your vehicle an enjoyable place. Keep the kids comfortable while they are secured in the child-restraint seats. For example, take off their shoes, socks, and heavier clothing.

➤ To help with motion sickness, make sure there is lots of fresh air inside your vehicle, have the kids focus their attention on the horizon, leave ample space between each child, engage them in activities to keep them busy, or drive at dawn and dusk to reduce their visual stimulation.

➤ Get your children involved in the vacation – let them gather books and pictures, not only about your destination, but also about the landscape en route.

➤ Give each child an inexpensive watch so that they can actually see the hours move forward.

➤ Special treat bags can be (secretly) made ahead of time and presented to your children while en route (kids love surprises).

➤ Give your kids specifics when they ask questions about getting there. Rather than responding, "Soon" or "We're close," engage in conversation such as "In 20 kilometres we'll be there. Now, let's sing a song about 20. Or, let's look for 20 red cars."

➤ Everyone needs quiet time, even when inside the vehicle. Let your kids know it's wind-down time. This gives them an opportunity to engage in creative mental play.

➤ Toys inside your vehicle should not have sharp edges. You and your kids could be injured in the event of a sudden stop, turn, or collision.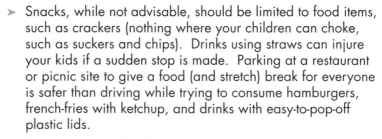

➤ Snacks, while not advisable, should be limited to food items, such as crackers (nothing where your children can choke, such as suckers and chips). Drinks using straws can injure your kids if a sudden stop is made. Parking at a restaurant or picnic site to give a food (and stretch) break for everyone is safer than driving while trying to consume hamburgers, french-fries with ketchup, and drinks with easy-to-pop-off plastic lids.

➤ Stop every 1 to 1½ hours to let the kids vent excess energy (and 'go to the bathroom'). Remember, it is probably uncomfortable (and often boring) for little folk to remain sedentary for more than an hour at a time.

Bringing Along The Pets

- Keep a not-too-tight collar around your pet's neck. The tags on the collar should include pet licence, pet's name, your phone number, and date of last rabies vaccination.

- Bring your pet's usual water. Often, unfamiliar water can disagree with your pet's stomach. Freeze a jug of water from home and top it up while en route to get your pet used to different water. You may also want to pack food your pet is used to.

- Make sure your pet has updated vaccinations. Bring along the health records, including a rabies certificate, especially if crossing the border.

- Secure your pet inside your vehicle in a carrier or with a specially designed belt system.

- Do not leave your pet inside your vehicle for an extended period of time. If you decide to leave your pet in the front or back seat, park in a shady area, partly open the windows, put lots of drinking water where your pet won't spill it, and don't stay away too long.

While On The Road

- Insure that you and all passengers wear seat belts. Instill the rule that there are no exceptions – wearing seat belts is a must.

- Ideally, all vehicle occupants should be in a good mood. It is never a good idea to get behind the wheel when you are emotionally upset.

- Be constantly aware of your surroundings.

- Maintain adequate ventilation throughout the interior of your vehicle; otherwise, fatigue can affect your concentration.

- Be aware how many hours you drive each day. Signs indicating that it's time to stop driving are: you get sleepy, your mood changes, you become easily distracted, and you pay less attention to traffic signs. Try to stop driving for the day at your regular bedtime hour.

- Most people have an internal body clock and feel sluggish between 2:00 p.m. - 5:00 p.m. and 2:00 a.m. - 6:00 a.m. Limit your driving time or don't drive at all during these periods.

- Ideally, pull into rest stops, restaurants, and gas stations where you do not have to cross the highway.

EVERYBODY IS
NICE AND
SECURE.....
MAKES ME HAPPY

- When stopped at gas stations, wipe the headlights and rear lights, wash all windows, check the oil, and look for fluid leaks underneath your vehicle.

- Do not rely on the air pump gauge at service stations. They often do not give an accurate air pressure reading for tires. Use a tire pressure gauge instead.

- Establish set days and times when you will call home to make sure all is okay and to let everyone know your location and that you are okay.

- If vacationing without your vehicle, disconnect the negative battery cable from the battery post. This may prevent "parasitic load" – when accessories continue using electricity even after the ignition is turned off - which can lead to a discharged battery.

Once At Your Vacation Destination

- Instill some safety precautions with your children:

    - Always have your children tell you where they are going, with whom, and how long you can expect them to be gone. Kids should never venture anywhere on their own; adventuring with a buddy is much safer and more enjoyable.

    - Show your kids how to dial 911, 611, *611, or the hotel operator.

    - Establish a meeting place if they become lost.

    - Let your kids know you will never be angry with them or punish them if they become lost. When they are found, keep the reunion positive.

    - Explain to your kids that they should always notice something that distinguishes their location or time of day (for example, a hill, a tall building, or where the sun is). Engage in this type of activity while driving to get your children accustomed to looking at their surroundings.

    - Teach your children to find a tree and hug it if they become lost. This makes them stay in one place and eases their anxiety so they can then think a bit more clearly.

    - Give each child a fanny pack for hiking and camping (see *Exterior of Vehicle*: "Trunk - Emergency Package"). Educate your kids on how to use what's in their fanny pack – the whistle is for noise, the garbage bag is for warmth, and so on.

    - Instill in your children that they should talk only to those who are uniformed, such as police officers, uniformed staff at theme parks, and anyone behind cash registers.

    - Teach your children to never talk to or go anywhere with strangers. Tell them that it is okay to hit a stranger and yell as loud as they can if a stranger touches them. The exception is when they are lost - any strangers yelling their name are good people.

- Most tourist offices have health and safety information about their particular area.

- While at campsites, ensure that your vehicle, tent, and other belongings are safely secured or hidden to avoid theft and vandalism.

- If you are vacationing without your vehicle and require a child-restraint seat, contact hospitals, the Red Cross, and health agencies. These places have government-approved child-restraint seats available for rent.

Section 7
The Mature Driver

Special Supplement

This section offers an updated view of the natural aging process as it relates to driving. Discussions centre on how individual adaptations can be made to benefit changes in your driving habits, traffic laws and control devices, and how vehicles are built. It all starts with attitude and there are ways to look at the driving experience in a more positive light.

SECTION SEVEN CONTENTS

Introduction

Driving involves using learned skills necessary for safe, responsible, and courteous behind the wheel manoeuvres. Knowledge about the rules of the road, coupled with the many years spent on the road, makes you a mature and experienced driver.

Yet, things change. Increased traffic congestion, updated road signs and symbols, and new technology in vehicles themselves often makes getting in the driver's seat an overwhelming experience. But, you do have a responsibility, - to yourself, your family, and all other motorists - to adapt to the changing environment of automobile travel.

Not to worry, though. There is a light at the end of the tunnel. By reviewing what you already know and by making individual modifications, you can resume control while behind the wheel.

AutoTalk for Women presents an overview on the various aspects of a vehicle - from dashboard components to the workings of the exhaust system. *Behind the Wheel* explores easy to master skills for getting back into positive driving habits. You may want to spend some time reviewing the preceding pages to regain a complete picture of the driving experience.

The pages that follow offer suggestions on restyling your approach to driving.

Have fun while on the road, women of wisdom!

The Driver's Seat

- The positions of the seat and seat belts were designed for an adult of average height and weight. A specially designed backrest, cushion, or pillow on the seat can provide the height needed to see clearly over the steering wheel and dashboard. Make sure the pillow does not slide around on the seat.

- Sitting higher on the seat also makes shoulder checking less of a strain on your body. Since you are in a position to see more clearly on either side and in front of and behind your vehicle, you don't have to turn your head from side to side as much.

- Most women feel they are too short, so they push the seat much too close to the steering wheel. The recommended minimum distance between the steering wheel and your chest is 25 to 30 cm (10 to 12 in.).

- Pedal extenders permanently fit over the brake, clutch, and gas pedals. These extenders are excellent for short-legged drivers who have trouble reaching the pedals.

- *How* you sit is just as important as *where* you sit. A straight back, with your hands on the steering wheel at the 9:00 and 3:00 positions, makes for a comfortable and safe seating position.

- Your comfort while in the driver's seat includes maintaining adequate airflow throughout the interior. Too hot of an interior usually makes you drowsy.

- The purpose of the head restraint is to help prevent whiplash if a collision occurs, so its position is important. Once you are safely seated in the driver's seat, position the head restraint. Then adjust the rear-view mirror so that you can see out the back window. The head restraint should never impede your vision when looking in the rear-view mirror.

- The rear-view mirror is imperative to use, both while driving and backing up. A wide-angle, curved rear-view mirror offers an expanded view of what is behind you.

- Side-view mirrors on the driver and passenger sides provide visibility on both sides of your vehicle - watch out for those blind spots, though. A smaller convex mirror can be installed on a corner of each side mirror.

What Your Vehicle Is Telling You

- Paint scratches, body dents, and rub marks on the tires can be visual indications of your driving manoeuvres.

  - Scratches on the sides of your vehicle may mean that you drive too close to parked vehicles or that you are scraping the side of the garage when you back out or drive in.

HOW UNUSUAL. A CLEAR PATH TO THE GARAGE. I'D BETTER DOUBLE CHECK.

➤ Dents anywhere on the body of your vehicle can indicate you are hitting the garage door when backing out or that your door hits a wall or another vehicle when you open it. This means you are parking too close to the building or vehicle.

➤ Rubs on the sides of the tires usually mean you are taking the curbs too close or are rubbing the tires when parking, especially parallel parking.

Purchasing New and Used Vehicles

• Many new vehicle designs include innovative safety features and additional comfort. However, there may be challenges for the mature driver with the way new vehicles are manufactured. Here are some points to consider when purchasing a new or used vehicle:

➤ When buying a new vehicle (or a used one from a dealership), have the sales associate show you *everything* about the vehicle. If necessary, book an appointment with a service representative who can show you what's under the hood and other aspects of your new investment. In a private purchase of a used vehicle, have the seller show you where everything is under the hood. Is the vehicle owner's manual in the glove compartment? It should be. You need this manual as it gives specifics about the vehicle, such as the type of engine oil to use.

➤ There are as many seat belt systems as there are makes of vehicles. Since you wear a seat belt every time you get behind the wheel, be comfortable with its fit and make sure it safely secures you across your chest and hips.

➤ Some vehicles have larger dashboard components, which makes glancing at them while you drive easier on the eyes.

➤ The colour and size of the dashboard can affect driving. Light-coloured dashboards can affect reflection, especially at night. The dashboard can also be so wide that it makes looking out the front windshield a challenge.

➤ Look for comfort and ease of use on devices, such as power locks, power windows, and power seats. Some power seats, for example, can be adjusted up and down, and forward and backward, to allow easier transfers in and out of the vehicle.

➤ The slope of the windshield can make seeing the front of the vehicle difficult.

➤ Tinted windows can affect your vision, especially at night. Some provincial (state) laws prohibit tinted windows on the front windshield and front side windows.

➤ Side-view mirrors with angled surfaces can help reduce blind spots. They don't eliminate them, though, so shoulder checking is still necessary.

➤ Onboard navigation systems offer convenience and safety features, especially in emergency situations.

Driving Recreational Vehicles

• Driving recreational vehicles (from van conversions to 10 m [34 ft.] motorhomes) require special driving skills.

• Your best course of action is to take two courses on recreational vehicles - one on manoeuvring while behind the wheel and another on RV maintenance. Check with an automobile club in your area for RV classes.

Rules of the Road

- Review the contents of an up-to-date driver's handbook, available from your local motor vehicle branch. For example, renew your knowledge of signs and shapes and what they mean. Recognize signs by their colour, such as green means "proceed, but with caution," not "okay, I'm going without looking." Learn to prioritize signs by their shapes. The red octagon shape of the stop sign, for example, is a regulatory sign, while the yellow diamond shape is a warning sign.

- Statistics indicate that most collisions occur close to one's home. Assess school and playground zones, speed limits, stop signs, lights, and other traffic legalities in your neighborhood. One recent change to school zones, for example, is the all year schools designated "All Year School" underneath the speed limit. Once you are familiar with what's close to your home, you can expand your knowledge to other areas in your community.

ONE POTATO, TWO POTATO, THREE POTATO, GO!'
HEH, HEH. A LITTLE SOMETHING FROM MY CHILDHOOD

- While driving, always keep in mind that traffic and other lights, such as warning lights, may not be working.

- Intersections remain one of the most common places for collisions. Intersections with stop signs, uncontrolled intersections, and controlled intersections with traffic lights all require different precautions. Stop signs mean just that – a complete stop is mandatory. Count to three after you stop to make sure your vehicle has come to a standstill. Giving the right-of-way to the vehicle on the right remains the standard at uncontrolled intersections. Turning left at traffic lights often results in a collision, as precautions are not taken to safely signal and then initiate the left turn.

Reasons for Driving

City Driving

- Ask yourself these questions:
    - ➤ I prefer to drive at a certain time of day?
    - ➤ Where do I drive – the supermarket, the shopping mall on Tuesdays for 10% off specials, or to visit the grandchildren?
    - ➤ Do I have a set route for each destination?
- As a mature driver, you often have flexibility of time. Avoid morning and evening rush-hour traffic; it's not worth the hassle.
- Modify your driving schedule to avoid poor street conditions due to heavy rain or snowfall.
- By taking a set route, you become familiar with speed limits, location of traffic lights, and other road rules. This makes you an expert in driving this route from "A" to "B" and is a smart move on your part - why make it more stressful driving in areas you are not familiar with. However, always be on the lookout for the unexpected, such as children running across the street.

Highway Driving

- Highways are not for the faint of heart. If you are uncomfortable with the speeds and amount of traffic, avoid driving on them. It is simply not worth the risk to you and other motorists to engage in a fast paced driving environment.
- Drive within the posted speed limits, not exceeding the limit nor driving too slowly. As a rule of thumb, stay within 10 km/h (6 mph) of the posted speed limit.

- If you make an annual highway trip, and have for years, you know the highway and all its idiosyncrasies. Take advantage of this knowledge. For example, make advance reservations at the accommodation you feel comfortable in, whether that's a hotel, motel, or RV campground. Plan to stop at that special restaurant that serves the best value-priced meal. You know what times of day you feel sleepy; schedule this stop at a familiar rest area.

- Eat a light breakfast before you spend a day of driving. A heavy meal first thing in the morning can make your stomach uncomfortable and you feel tired. Save the indulgences for when you finish driving for the day.

- Night driving involves adjusting your vision. Also, semi-trailers and other heavy trucks are often on the road at night - at the best of times you want to avoid driving behind or passing these types of vehicles.

- Give yourself lots of time to get from home to your final destination.

- If you are highway driving and you see that there is a convoy of vehicles behind you, pull into the next service centre or town (on your side of the road only, never make unnecessary left turns on a highway). Do not pull onto the shoulder to let vehicles pass. Not only is it unsafe, in some provinces (states), it is illegal to drive on the shoulder of the highway, except in emergency situations, such as a flat tire.

Driving Habits

- The following points offer behind the wheel manoeuvres and other skills necessary for driving safely, responsibly, and courteously.

  - As a rule of thumb, use the centre lane only for turning left. Otherwise, stay in right-hand lane as much as possible.

  - Always engage the right or left turn-signal light to indicate an upcoming turn or lane change. You can never use the signal arm too much.

  - When changing lanes, always shoulder check before you start moving your vehicle into the other lane. You don't have to turn your upper body, but you do need to turn your head. If you move your upper body to shoulder check, your hands tend to also move in the same direction. You don't want this to happen while your hands are on the steering wheel!

  - Maintain a safe distance between you and the vehicle ahead. As a rule of thumb, always have lots of pavement between you and the vehicle in front, regardless if city or highway driving.

  - Talking while driving can be a distraction. Your primary job while behind the wheel is to focus on the road. If you are uncomfortable engaging in conversation while driving, tell your passenger(s). You may want to turn off the radio as well, and definitely never talk on a cell phone while driving.

  - Backing up is never easy to accomplish. Always back up slowly - it is easier to control your vehicle when moving at a speed less than 5 km/h (3 mph). Better yet, try to park where you don't have to back up, especially in shopping centres and grocery store parking lots.

➤ When driving, we all have a tendency to look where we *don't* want to go. Always look where you *do* want to go, whether making a turn, changing lanes, or if your vehicle is skidding.

➤ When merging, you should never have to come to a complete stop. What you must have is the confidence and determination to get into the flow of traffic.

➤ Look all around while driving, not just at what is in front of you:

■ Look well ahead of your vehicle – about one block when city driving.

■ Scan what is on the sides of your vehicle by turning your head slightly from side to side, rather than using only your eyes. Use the side-view mirrors to also glance at what's to the sides of your vehicle.

■ By constantly glancing in the rear-view mirror, you always know what is behind you.

➤ If your driving record indicates numerous tickets and infractions, it is important you reevaluate your present situation, taking into consideration changes in your eyesight, hearing, and dexterity.

➤ An excellent way to assess your driving habits and improve your driving skills is to participate in a driver refresher course. Having an unbiased individual look at your driving abilities and habits can be very helpful. Did you know that the most common mistakes mature drivers make involve signalling and shoulder checking (lack of), merging deficiencies, stopping (failing to), and hand placement on the steering wheel? Most of us believe we are better drivers than we actually are. A *good* driver is one who knows that improvements can be made, is willing to listen, and then participates in making constructive changes.

Physical Health

Vision

- As you mature, your eyes reflect what and how much you see. When driving, attention to detail, colour distinctions, constantly moving objects, depth perception (how close or how far an object is), and peripheral vision (seeing to the sides, while looking ahead) can pose challenges. Here are a few suggestions to help you better see what's on the road.

  > Driving with low beams, rather than daytime running lights (DRL) offers improved visibility. Low beams also light up the dashboard, whereas most DRL do not. As well, other motorists are able to see you more clearly because low beams light up the rear of your vehicle as well as the front. Most vehicles with DRL do not light up the back of your vehicle.

  > To adjust to the headlights, street and other lights while night driving and on overcast days, give your eyes one minute to focus on the landscape before you start driving.

  > Eyewear is vital in your ability to see. Consider the following to improve your vision while behind the wheel:

    ■ Prescription glasses; possibly two sets - one for day driving and another if you frequently drive at night.

    ■ Superior-quality sunglasses (consider prescription sunglasses) are a must on bright sunny days. Never wear sunglasses at night.

    ■ Choose eyewear and sunglasses that have narrow side temples - wide sides distract from your ability to see from side to side. Also, with narrow temples, you don't have to turn your head as much to shoulder check.

- Keep an extra pair of glasses in the glove compartment.

- Have your eyesight routinely checked by your optometrist. If you are experiencing vision changes or discomfort, let her or him know. Early prevention and treatment are the key words here.

Hearing

- If you have trouble hearing, you must remain visually aware of what's on the road. For example, emergency vehicles, such as an ambulance, rely on your sense of sound as well as sight. Remember, a flashing red or blue light means you should move over to let the unit pass you.

- After using the turn-signal arm, visually check the dashboard to make sure the green arrow is no longer flashing.

- Hearing aids are now more sensitive to sound. Decide, with your doctor, if now is the time to invest in one.

Bones and Other Body Parts

- As you mature, your bones become more porous, brittle and less flexible. If you are in a collision, then, a bone can easily break and the injured part may take a long time to heal.

- Joint stiffness and pain, such as arthritis in the hands, can limit how quickly you turn the steering wheel. Consider installing a padded steering wheel cover so that you can grasp the steering wheel more firmly.

- A surgery, fracture, mild stroke, closed head injury, dizzy spells, or sudden pains to your chest all affect your ability to drive. The time needed to recuperate may mean you stay away from the driver's seat for a period of time.

Medications (Prescription and Non-Prescription)

- Mixing different prescriptions together can have adverse effects, especially on vision. Check with your doctor or pharmacist if you are taking more than one medication at a time.

- Non-prescription drugs, such as cough syrup and cold pills, affect concentration levels. Talk with your doctor or pharmacist regarding the side effects of medications.

- Before taking any medications, read carefully the instructions on all medications, especially their side effects, such as causing drowsiness or blurred vision.

- Never exceed the dosage prescribed by your physician.

- Never leave medications in the glove compartment.

- Keep all medications in their original containers and the receipts and information sheet of all prescriptions in your purse.

- If you use syringes for medical reasons, carry extras with you, but do not leave them inside your vehicle.

Frame of Mind

Mental Alertness

- Most people feel sluggish between 2:00 p.m. - 5:00 p.m. and 2:00 a.m. - 6:00 a.m. Know your daily low points and avoid driving during these times.

- Pay special attention if you did not get enough sleep the night before. It is never a good idea to get behind the wheel when tired.

- Driving is a sedentary activity, but you must be mentally alert. Keeping physically fit helps keep the mind "alive" as well as maintaining healthy bones and other body parts.

- Drink water! Research studies have found that there is a connection between water intake and improved concentration. Always carry a cold bottle of water while driving – you'll be more refreshed than if you drink caffeine and sugared liquids.

- To ease tension before and after driving, try this relaxation technique either sitting or standing: extend both arms out in front of you; cross your left wrist over your right wrist; interlace your fingers; and draw the hands up towards your chest. Close your eyes and deep breath for one minute. Do the same technique crossing your right wrist over the left wrist.

- Dealing with losses, such as a family member moving or the death of a spouse or friend often reduces your level of alertness and concentration. Other changes relating to memory and orientation can affect your judgement skills. Discuss these and other concerns with your doctor and ask her or him for driving guidelines.

I AM WHO I AM, AND NOT
JUST PART OF THE CROWD

THESE GLASSES ARE THE FINISHING TOUCH ON A FINE WORK OF ART.... ME!!

Attitude

- Never overestimate your abilities. There is always room for improvement, no matter how good a driver you believe you are.

- At some point in your life, it is time to hang up the keys. Get your family and friends involved in the decision-making process. You could even have a "I'm Hangin' Up The Keys" party! This is, indeed, another rite of passage and your positive outlook deserves a celebration. Creative ideas, such as this, often stimulate new ways to enhance your independence.

- Anger equates with road rage. You don't ever want to be called "one of those out-of-control angry motorists."

- Talk about your driving concerns. Find someone you are comfortable with to share your thoughts, ideas, and feelings. That individual can be a neighbour, pastor, professional counselor, medical specialist, or your weekly bridge-playing group.

- Reminisce with family and friends about your positive experiences behind the wheel. Good auto stories are meant to be shared.

- It is not your responsibility to worry about what other people are doing while behind the wheel. Concern yourself with your driving abilities. When you drive in a safe, responsible, and courteous manner, you hope (and expect) that other motorists will do the same for you. At times, though, your patience is necessary, just as other drivers must sometimes be patient with you.

It all starts with you.

Section **8**
Conversions

SECTION EIGHT CONTENTS

Celsius - Fahrenheit

From Celsius to Fahrenheit

- 0°C = 32°F

Calculation from Celsius to Fahrenheit

1. Multiply the Celsius temperature by 9
2. Divide by 5
3. Add 32

> Example: **20°C** = 20 x 9 = 180
> divided by 5 = 36 + 32 = **68° F**

From Fahrenheit to Celsius

- 32°F = 0°C

Calculation from Fahrenheit to Celsius

1. Subtract 32 from the Fahrenheit temperature
2. Multiply by 5
3. Divide by 9

> Example: **-20°F** = -20 – 32 = -52 x 5 = -260
> divided by 9 = **-29°C**

Body Temperature

- 37°C = 98.4°F

Centimetres - Inches

From Centimetres to Inches

- 1 millimetre = 0.039 inches
- 1 centimetre = 0.39 inches
- 1 metre = 3.28 feet or 1.09 yards

Calculation from centimetres to inches

1. Multiply millimetres, centimetres, or metres by inches, feet, or yards, depending on which unit you use.
   - Example: **12 centimetres** = 12 x 0.39 = **4.7 inches**
   - Example: **3 metres** = 3 x 3.28 = **9.84 feet**

From Inches to Centimetres

- 1 inch = 25.4 millimetres
- 1 inch = 2.54 centimetres
- 1 foot = 0.3 metres
- 1 yard = 0.91 metres

Calculation from inches to centimetres

1. Multiply inches, feet, or yards by millimetres, centimetres, or metres, depending on which unit you use.
   - Example: **30 inches** = 30 x 2.54 = **76.2 centimetres**
   - Example: **8 feet** = 8 x 0.3 = **2.4 metres**

Kilograms - Pounds

From Kilograms to Pounds

- 1 kilogram = 2.20 pounds

Calculation from kilograms to pounds

1. Multiply the kilograms by 2
2. Add 10%
   - Example: **160 kilograms** = 160 x 2 = 320
     + 10% = 320 + 32 = **352 pounds**

From Pounds to Kilograms

- 1 pound = 0.45 kilograms

Calculation from pounds to kilograms

1. Divide the pounds by 2
2. Subtract 10%
   - Example: **400 pounds** = 400 divided by 2 = 200
     – 10% = 200 – 20 = **180 kilograms**

Kilometres - Miles

From Kilometres to Miles

• 1 kilometre = 0.62 miles

Calculation from kilometres to miles

1. Divide kilometres by 3
2. Multiply by 2
   ➤ Example: **60 kilometres** = 60 divided by 3 = 20
   x 2 = **40 miles**

From Miles to Kilometres

• 1 mile = 1.61 kilometers

Calculation from miles to kilometres

1. Take mileage to ones or tens
2. Multiply by 6
3. Add to mileage
   ➤ Example: **60 miles** = 6 x 6 = 36 + 60 = **96 kilometres**

Litres - Gallons

From Litres to Gallons

- 1 litre = 0.88 imperial quarts
- 1 litre = 0.22 imperial gallons

Calculation from litres to gallons

    1. Multiply litres by quarts or gallons, depending on which unit you use.

       ➤ Example: **6 litres** = 6 x 0.88 = **5.28 quarts**

From Gallons to Litres

- 1 imperial quart = 1.14 litres
- 1 imperial gallon = 4.54 litres

Calculation from gallons to litres

    - Multiply quarts or gallons by litres

       ➤ Example: **9 quarts** = 9 x 1.14 = **10.26 litres**

Section 9

AutoTalk Assistant

Section Nine Contents

Vehicle Specifications Record

Cut this out, attach to a colour photograph of your vehicle, and place inside your wallet or purse

Year: _____   Make: _____

Model: _____   Colour: _____

Engine Size (litres): _____   Cylinders: _____

Torque (lb./ft.): _____

Horsepower (hp): _____

Air Conditioning: ☐ Yes   ☐ No

Vehicle Identification Number (VIN): _____

Licence Plate Number: _____

Ignition Key Number: _____

Insurance Company Name: _____

Telephone Number: _____

Policy Number: _____

Emergency Name Contact Information

Fill in the blanks and leave this information in the book.

Note: Include the area code for all phone numbers. Addresses are not necessary (for confidentiality reasons).

Main contact person:

Name (first name only): _____

Home: ( ) _____ Work: ( ) _____

Cellular: ( ) _____

Secondary contact person:

Name (first name only): _____

Home: ( ) _____ Work: ( ) _____

Cellular: ( ) _____

Motor Association Membership Number: _____

Local Phone Number: ( ) _____

National Phone Number: ( ) _____

Towing Company Name: _____

Phone Number: ( ) _____

Vehicle Insurance Company Name: _____

Policy Number: _____

Phone Number: ( ) _____

cont'd on other side

Emergency Name Contact Information

Doctor's Name: _____

Phone Number: (   ) _____

Emergency Phone Number: (   ) _____

Pediatrician's Name: _____

Phone Number: (   ) _____

Emergency Phone Number: (   ) _____

Pharmacy's Name: _____

Phone Number: (   ) _____

Hospital Name: _____

Emergency Ward: (   ) _____

Poison Centre:

Phone Number: (   ) _____

Distress (Emergency Calls) Phone Numbers: 911, *611, 611, or 411

Local Police:

Phone Number: (   ) _____

RCMP (Highway Patrol)

Phone Number: (   ) _____

Non Emergency Department:

Fire Department Phone Number: (   ) _____

Leaving Vehicle to Walk

If you are leaving your vehicle to walk, fill out this placard (print clearly), and place it on the dashboard of your vehicle, not on the outside windshield.

LEAVING VEHICLE TO WALK

Today's Date: _____

Time you left your vehicle: _____A.M. _____P.M.

Your Name: (First)_____ (Last) _____

Name of Contact Person: _____

Home: (   ) _____ Work: (   ) _____

Cellular: (   ) _____

How many adults are with you: _____

Number of Children?: _____ Ages: _____

Are you injured?: ☐ Yes   ☐ No

Is anyone else injured?: ☐ Yes   ☐ No

If yes, detail the injury: _____

Do you have any food?: ☐ Yes   ☐ No

If yes, how much?: _____

Do you have water?: ☐ Yes   ☐ No

If yes, how much?: _____

What direction are you headed? (be specific): _____

_____

What signs will you be leaving behind (e.g. flagging trees)?: _____

_____

Getting Inside Another Vehicle

If you are leaving your vehicle to get inside another vehicle, fill out this placard (print clearly), cut it from this book and place it on the dashboard of your vehicle, not on the outside windshield.

✂ --

GETTING INSIDE ANOTHER VEHICLE

Today's Date: _____

Time you left your vehicle: _____ A.M. _____ P.M.

Your Name: (First)_____ (Last) _____

Name of Contact Person: _____

Home: (   ) _____ Work: (   ) _____

Cellular: (   ) _____

Information of the person you are travelling with
Note: If the individual is not willing to give this information,
DO NOT *get inside her or his vehicle.*

Name: (First)_____ (Last) _____

Address - Street:_____City: _____

Home: (   ) _____ Work: (   ) _____

Cellular: (   ) _____

Driver's Licence Number: _____

Physical description of vehicle and driver: _____

_____

What is your destination? What is your direction of travel? Be specific:

_____

_____

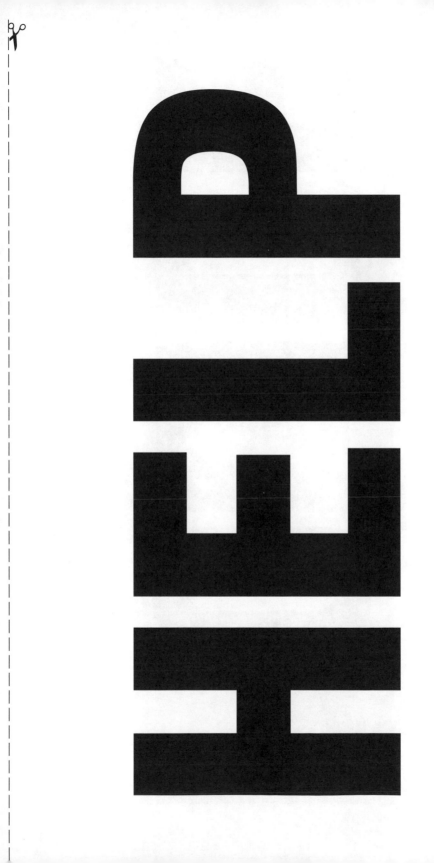

POLICE

Maintenance Log Sheet

Date	Mileage	Repairs	Name of Shop/ Dealership	Name of Mechanic/ Service Representative	Phone

Maintenance Log Sheet

Date	Mileage	Repairs	Name of Shop/ Dealership	Name of Mechanic/ Service Representative	Phone

Collision Report

Complete the following information at the time of collision

Your Vehicle

Insurance company name: _____

Phone number( ) _____

Policy number_____ Expiry date _____

Licence plate number _____

Your driver's licence number_____

Expiry date _____ Class _____ Condition Code/End (letter) _____

Damage to your vehicle (where, extent of damage) _____

Other Vehicles - Vehicle 1

Name of driver: First _____ Last _____

Address of driver: Street _____

City _____ Postal Code (Zip) _____

Phone numbers:

Home ( ) _____ Work ( ) _____ Cellular ( ) _____

Driver's licence number_____

Expiry date _____ Class _____ Condition Code/End (letter) _____

Vehicle: Year_____ Make _____ Model _____ Colour _____

Vehicle licence plate number _____

Vehicle registration number _____

Insurance company name _____

Phone number ( ) _____

Policy number _____ Expiry date _____

Damage to vehicle 1 _____

(cont'd on next page)

Collision Report (cont'd)

Other Vehicles - Vehicle 2

Name of driver: First _____ Last _____

Address of driver: Street _____

City _____ Postal Code (Zip) _____

Phone numbers:

Home ( ) _____ Work ( ) _____ Cellular ( ) _____

Driver's licence number_____

Expiry date _____ Class _____ Condition Code/End (letter) _____

Vehicle: Year _____ Make _____ Model _____ Colour _____

Vehicle licence plate number _____

Vehicle registration number _____

Insurance company name _____

Phone number ( ) _____

Policy number _____ Expiry date _____

Damage to vehicle 2 _____

_____

Diagram of Collision Scene:

(cont'd on next page)

Collision Report (cont'd)

Write down the events leading to the accident. Be as specific as possible

Date of collision _____   _____   _____
month   day   year

Time of collision   A.M. _____ P.M. _____

Location of collision (be specific) _____

_____

Weather _____

Road conditions _____

Traffic congestion _____

Traffic signals or signs _____

Specifics about your vehicle

Direction of your travel _____

Skid marks: Yes ____ No ____ Distance of skid marks _____

Your speed _____ Accurate: Yes __ No ___ Estimated: Yes __ No __

Your intentions at the time (e.g., signalling for a turn) _____

Other remarks (e.g., low/high beams on, brake lights working, did you slow down, seat belts engaged)

_____

_____

_____

_____

(cont'd on next page)

Collision Report (cont'd)

Specifics about other vehicle(s)

Direction of other vehicle(s) _____

Skid marks: Yes ____ No ____ Distance of skid marks _____

Other vehicle(s) speed _____   Accurate: Yes ___ No ___

Estimated: Yes ___ No ___

Other vehicle(s) intentions at the time (e.g., signalling for a turn)_____

Other remarks (e.g., low/high beams on, brake lights working, did they slow down, seat belts engaged)

_____

_____

_____

Vehicle Occupants

Your Vehicle

Name of occupant: First _____ Last _____

Phone number of occupant (   ) _____

Injuries: Yes _____ No _____

If yes give, describe injury and its extent _____

_____

Other Vehicle(s)

Name of occupant: First _____ Last _____

Phone number of occupant (   ) _____

Injuries: Yes _____ No _____

If yes give, describe injury and its extent _____

_____

(cont'd on next page)

Collision Report (cont'd)

Any pedestrians associated with the collision? Yes _____ No _____

If yes, give a description and extent of the injury _____

_____

Your story

In your own words write down everything relating to the collision, even if you think it is irrelevant.

_____

_____

_____

_____

_____

_____

_____

_____

_____

_____

_____

_____

_____

_____

_____

_____

(cont'd on next page)

Collision Report (cont'd)

Police Officers

Names of officer(s) _____

Badge number(s) _____

Collision file number _____

Emergency Personnel

Name(s) _____

Witnesses

Witness 1

Name _____

Phone numbers:

Home (   ) _____ Work (   ) _____ Cellular (   ) _____

Witness 2

Name _____

Phone numbers:

Home (   ) _____ Work (   ) _____ Cellular (   ) _____

Witness 3

Name _____

Phone numbers:

Home (   ) _____ Work (   ) _____ Cellular (   ) _____

(cont'd on next page)

Collision Report (cont'd)

Witness 1 statement:

Witness 2 statement:

Witness 3 statement:

Unoccupied Vehicle Collision Report

If you damage a vehicle that is unoccupied, fill in this report, cut off the bottom portion, and leave it on the front windshield of the damaged vehicle.

Information on the vehicle you hit:

Year _____ Make _____ Model _____ Colour _____

Specific description of damage _____

Detail existing dents, scrapes, etc., on vehicle _____

_____

(Cut here and leave this part on the front windshield of the damaged vehicle).

✂ -

Today's date _____ _____ _____
                  month   day   year

Time: A.M. ____ P.M. ____

Your name: First _____ Last _____

Phone numbers:
Home (   ) _____ Work (   ) _____ Cellular (   ) _____

I caused the following damage to your vehicle: _____

_____

_____

_____

_____

_____

HOME CHECKLIST

Before you leave for a business trip or vacation, review this pre-departure checklist and include any specifics relating to your home.

Fill out the "Emergency Name Contact Sheet" and the "Home Sitter Task List."

Pre-Departure Checklist

- Lock all windows and doors.
- Set timer lights in some upstairs, main floor, and basement rooms.
- Unplug televisions, stereos, computers, unused lamps, and other electrical appliances, such as the toaster.
- Put the hot water tank to the vacation setting.
- Remove all house keys hidden outside.
- Turn off all outside faucets.
- Stop newspaper delivery.
- Leave house key and mailbox key with home sitter.
- Additional notes _____

_____

_____

Added Precautions

1. If you have a home security system, let the dispatch centre know of your plans. Let them know that a home sitter will visit your home regularly to check it and give it that "lived-in" look.

2. Complete the "Emergency Name Contact Information" sheet and leave with your home sitter along with the "Home Sitter Task List."

3. Extra precautions are necessary during winter. Pipes can freeze, resulting in burst waterlines, especially if water is not running through the pipes. On a daily basis, have your home sitter turn on all the hot and cold water taps in your home for a few minutes and flush every toilet. Check the thermostat to ensure that adequate heat is maintained throughout your home. Check the furnace to be sure the pilot light is still on.

Home Sitter Information List

Fill out the "Emergency Name Contact Information" sheet, cut this
page from the book, and leave it with the individual in charge of
taking care of your home while you are away.

Emergency Name Contact Sheet

Main contact person:

First name _____ Last name _____

Phone numbers:

Home _____ Work _____ Cellular _____

Second contact person:

First name _____ Last name _____

Phone numbers:

Home _____ Work _____ Cellular _____

Home security company

Name _____

Phone _____

Code _____

Police non-emergency number: _____

Emergency number: 911

(cont'd on other side)

Home Sitter Task List

Check the house twice a day - morning and evening

- Open upstairs window coverings in the morning. In the evening, close all window coverings.

- Water all inside plants every few days.

- Weather permitting, water the lawn and outside plants.

- If it snowed, shovel the driveway and walk.

- Bring in newspapers and flyers left on doorstep.

- Bring in the mail.

- Walk around inside and outside of house to check for signs of attempted break-in.

- Additional responsibilities: _____

_____

_____

_____

_____

_____

_____

_____

Book Order Form

Customer Information

Ship to:	Bill to:
First Name _____	First Name _____
Last Name _____	Last Name _____
Street _____	Street _____
Street _____	Street _____
City _____	City _____
Province (State) _____	Province (State) _____
Postal code (Zip) _____	Postal code (Zip) _____
Telephone ( ) _____	Telephone ( ) _____
E-mail address _____	E-mail address _____

Title	Quantity	Price	Total
AutoTalk for Women		x $19.95 (Cdn)	
AutoTalk for Women		x $14.95 (U.S.)	
		Sub-total:	
GST# 87326-4220-RT0001 GST 7% of Sub-total (Canada only):			
		Shipping & Handling:	$4.00
		Total enclosed:	

Payment method

☐ Check (payable to Horse & Musket Ltd.)   ☐ Money Order

Mail order to:

Horse & Musket Ltd.
Box 811, Station M, Calgary, Alberta
Canada T2P 2J6
E-mail: musket@attcanada.net
Phone: 1.877.258.9285
(Please allow 3 - 4 weeks for delivery)

An Invitation

Do you have an automotive story to tell?

You are invited to write a one- to two-page narrative about a driving experience. The story can be funny, enlightening, or more serious in content. Just tell me about what you've encountered behind the wheel or as a passenger.

You can write about what one of your kids did in the rear seat, how you survived a collision because of your quick thinking, or that unforgettable family car trip - the stories are endless, I'm sure.

Are you a mechanic? Then, I *know* you have a tale or two to tell about your experiences!

Upon receipt of your story, your name will be automatically entered in a draw for some fabulous "women type" prizes. If your story is chosen, it will appear in an upcoming automotive stories book. Your name will appear as a contributor and you will receive a complimentary copy of the book.

So, ladies, put pen to paper or fingers to keyboard and send your story to:

Shirley Kachur
Horse & Musket Ltd.
Box 811, Station M
Calgary, Alberta
Canada T2P 2J6
E-mail: musket@attcanada.net

Remember to include your name, address, telephone number, and e-mail address.

I am already excited about hearing from you!